microwave
systems
planning

microwave
systems
planning

KENNETH L. DUMÁS AND LEO G. SANDS

HAYDEN BOOK COMPANY, INC., NEW YORK

Preface

IT is the purpose of this book to provide a volume defining and explaining, in a semitechnical manner, the most important criteria involved in the planning, engineering, and installation of microwave equipment used for communication purposes. The discussion will be confined to point-to-point FM systems.

The increasing growth of population in the United States as well as the rest of the world, coupled with the stepped-up pace of business transactions, has tremendously stimulated the demand for rapid communication facilities. For years this demand has been handled by the addition of multiplex equipment to open wire and cable facilities, placing severe economic burdens upon the various enterprises needing these facilities for toll service or for carrying on their day-to-day activities. In recent years the widespread business use of computers by large companies has served to increase the requirements for modern and timely communications, since computers must be fed large amounts of information that must often be gathered from all over the country. Computerization coupled with the very wide bandwidth requirements of TV has thus forced the rapid development of new equipment for use in microwave systems.

This book was written to be used by management people and engineers who may not have a communication background as well as by communication engineers. It will acquaint the former with the factors that must be considered in the application of point-to-point microwave to their communication needs and at the same time provide the latter with a comprehensive source of reference data for microwave systems planning.

The coverage of the subject is complete enough to make possible the engineering of an average point-to-point system. No attempt has been made to exhaust the vast number of intricate variables that may be encountered on any particular task. For instance, weather has a marked influence on microwave propagation, and a study of meteorological effects alone could fill several books. Information relating to optical phenomena is equally important to the satisfactory operation of microwave equipment and likewise very complex. Thus, when consideration is given to items such as line-of-sight path clearance, which requires an understanding of the Fresnel phenomenon, the information provided is merely a condensation of the many wide-ranging studies of the phenomenon important to the successful engineering of point-to-point systems.

The nomenclature, phraseology, and symbols employed in this book are those most commonly encountered in the telephone business because the greatest use of microwave communication equipment is found in those industries that follow telephone practice. The opening chapters deal mostly with the theoretical aspects of the subject, progressing from frequency and wave theory, including propagation, to hardware theory. Subsequent chapters investigate the practical aspects of establishing a microwave path with a high probability of good performance.

Kenneth L. Dumás
Leo. G. Sands

Contents

1

Fundamentals of Microwave Theory

Microwaves are a result of the highest radio frequencies commonly used for communication, detection, control, and navigation. Through general usage, the term *microwave* has come to mean those wavelengths that are so short that "surface waves" and reflections from the ionosphere occur but that are still long enough to prevent atomic and molecular resonances from occurring in the gaseous components of the atmosphere.

Within the microwave region, the relation of the signal wavelength to the size of material objects at the system terminals and along or near the transmission path is of primary importance to the properties of transmission. Most of these objects are comparable in size to the wavelength in the microwave region; many are much larger. As a consequence, it is necessary to discard some of the concepts employed in radio engineering at the longer wavelengths and substitute some of the techniques and language normally associated with optics and specifically devised to handle the situation in the optical portion of the electromagnetic spectrum.

Wavelength and Frequency

Both *wavelength* and *frequency* are often used to refer to a particular portion of the microwave spectrum. The two terms are broadly equivalent, because a definite relationship exists between them. Electrical energy is propagated into space as a result of the electrical and magnetic stress that is set up in the transmission medium. In the case of radio energy, this stress

1

rapidly alternates from one polarity to the other at the frequency established by the current generators. The distance occupied by one cycle of such an alternating wave is called a wavelength; it is equal to the velocity of the wave divided by the number of cycles propagated each second, hereafter called Hertz. The relation between the wavelength (λ) in meters and frequency (f) in Hertz (Hz) is therefore:

$$\lambda = \frac{300,000,000}{f} \tag{1}$$

The quantity 300,000,000 is the velocity of light in meters per second. Since the frequencies encountered in microwave systems are well into the megahertz region, a more common form of the formula is:

$$\lambda = \frac{300}{f} \tag{2}$$

in which case f is equal to the frequency in MHz.

Electromagnetic Waves

Transfer of electromagnetic energy in a medium depends on certain electromagnetic properties of the medium as well as on similar properties of the boundary medium. Thus, wave transfer in the atmosphere depends in some degree upon the characteristics of the earth over which transmission takes place and their effect on the atmosphere above. These properties are defined by the following three major parameters:

(1) *Dielectric constant* (ϵ): The amount of electrostatic energy which can be stored by any particular medium. A dielectric is an insulating material such as air, rubber, glass, paper, and the like. The dielectric constant for a vacuum is equal to 8.854×10^{-12} farads per meter.

(2) *Permeability* (μ): The measure of the superiority of a material over a vacuum as a path for magnetic lines of force. Ferromagnetic materials such as iron, steel, nickel, and other magnetic alloys all have high permeabilities. Conversely, diamagnetic materials such as copper, brass, and bismuth have permeabilities comparable to that of free space. The value of μ for a vacuum is equal to 1.257×10^{-6} henrys per meter.

(3) *Conductivity* (σ): The measure of the ability of a material to pass electrical energy. All pure metals are good conductors, with some having less resistance than others. Conductivity is the reciprocal of resistivity and is measured in mhos. Although σ is zero in a vacuum, ϵ and μ never are; in fact, the velocity of an electromagnetic wave in any medium is given by:

$$v = 1 / \sqrt{\mu\epsilon} \tag{3}$$

in which:

v = velocity, in meters per second

ϵ = the dielectric constant of the material through which the wave is propagated

μ = the permeability of the material through which the wave must pass

The values of μ and ϵ for dry homogeneous air are essentially the same as for a vacuum, and it will be found that the velocity of propagation of electromagnetic waves through both materials is approximately 3×10^8 meters per second, or 186,000 miles per second.

When electromagnetic waves are propagated into space, there are two major fields of interest. These are the *electric field,* commonly referred to as the E field, and the *magnetic field,* called the H field. The direction of the E field normally establishes the polarization of the wave, and when this field is in a vertical plane, the wave is said to be *vertically polarized.* If the E field is in a horizontal plane, the wave is classified as *horizontally polarized.* The velocity of propagation is unaffected by the polarization of the wave, but as will be seen later, the polarization will considerably affect reflected waves.

Wave Propagation

The simplest antenna or radiator is a theoretical point source commonly referred to as an *isotropic radiator.* In unobstructed space, such a source radiates equally well in all directions, and the electrical energy propagated will progress at the speed of light (186,000 miles per second). Therefore, after 1 millisecond, the field of energy will be present at a distance of 186 miles from the source. Similarly, at the end of 1 second the field of energy will have formed a sphere with a radius of 186,000 miles. In each instance the spherical wave forms a front surface (or wave) with the isotropic radiator at the center. According to Christian Huygens, such a wave front may be considered to consist of an infinite number of isotropic radiators, each one sending out self-generated waves away from the source, as in Fig. 1-1.[1]

As such a wave front advances, a small section of its face appears to be a plane. Both the electric field intensity *(E)* and the magnetic field intensity *(H)* would be vectors perpendicular to each other and located in the plane wave front.

Reflection and Refraction

By studying the changes in a wave front that occur as a wave advances through a medium of one density, it is possible to predict the effects that will

---

[1]*Radiation Laboratory Series,* No. 13, McGraw-Hill Book Co., New York, Chap. 6.

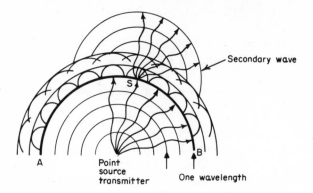

FIG. 1-1.　HUYGENS' THEOREM

Along the primary wavefront AB radiating from the point source transmitter an infinite number of points are excited. Each of these points radiates in phase with the primary wave and also radiates secondary waves such as that shown coming from point S. These secondary waves combine to form a new wavefront that progresses in the same direction of propagation.

occur when a wave encounters a medium of a different density which either *reflects, refracts,* or *absorbs* energy.

Since we are dealing with the transfer of electromagnetic energy when considering wave propagation, it is convenient to express the energy relations of the incident and reflected waves by a ratio called the *coefficient of reflection.*

The coefficient of reflection *(p)* is defined as the square root of a power ratio. It is found by dividing the *reflected* energy per second leaving a reflecting surface by the energy per second *incident* to the same surface. If the two values of energy are the same *(p = 1)*, the surface is a perfect reflector. If the reflected energy is smaller than the incident energy, the missing quantity is either dissipated at the reflecting surface, or partially dissipated and partially passed through the surface as a *refracted* ray.

For example, when an electromagnetic wave impinges upon a cloud, most of the energy passes through the cloud. But, due to various particles of moisture in the cloud, part of the wave is returned by reflection at the surface, whereas another part is absorbed within the cloud itself. When the wave energy is absorbed, it is converted into heat. The part of a wave that is passed through the cloud will be refracted, or changed in direction, if the electromagnetic properties of the cloud differ from those of the surrounding air. In fact, when a radio wave encounters any medium whose properties differ from those of the previous medium, reflection and refraction take place simultaneously.

Refraction is the result of a change in velocity of an electromagnetic wave as it passes from one medium to another. If the density of the foreign

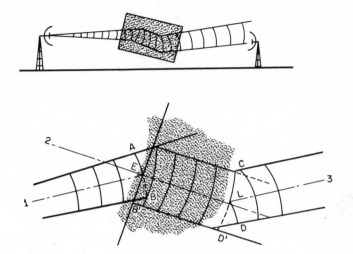

FIG. 1-2.   REFRACTED WAVE

Since the air mass shown is denser than the surrounding air, the micro-wave beam is slowed down as it enters and speeded up as it leaves. If the dense air had not been present, point B' would have progressed at its normal velocity to point B. But since the velocity is less in denser air, centerline 2 and wave EB' show its new direction. As the wave leaves the denser medium, it is again speeded up. Wavefront LD and centerline 3 show its final direction.

medium is less than that of the surrounding medium, the speed of the portion of the wave passing through will increase, and the wave will bend away from its former centerline in a downward direction.

If the density of the foreign medium is greater than that surrounding it, the speed of the wave will decrease. This will cause the wave to bend away from its centerline in an upward direction. For this reason the law of refraction states that an incident wave traveling obliquely from one medium to another will change direction if the velocity of the wave in one medium is different from that in the other, as illustrated in Fig. 1-2. It has been shown that the ratio of the sine of the angle of incidence to the sine of the angle of refraction is the same as the ratio of the respective wave velocities in these media. Acording to Snell's law, this is expressed mathematically, as follows:

$$\eta = \frac{sin\ i}{sin\ r} \quad \text{or} \quad \eta = \frac{v_1}{v_2} \tag{4}$$

Here, η is called the *index of refraction* of the second medium relative to the first. The absolute index of refraction of any material or gas is its index with respect to a vacuum and is practically equivalent to the value with respect to air. Thus if the velocity of a wave is v in a particular substance, v_o in a vacuum, and v_a in air, the index of refraction is given by the formula:

$$\eta = \frac{v_o}{v} \qquad (5)$$

which is practically equivalent to:

$$\eta = \frac{v_a}{v} \qquad (6)$$

The absolute value of the refraction index is not nearly so important to microwave propagation as the change of the refractive index.[1] This will be discussed more fully later in a more direct microwave application.

Diffraction

Wave reflections rarely originate at a single point. According to *Huygens'* principle, they radiate from the entire surface of an obstacle which is in the path of the wave (see Fig. 1-1). As secondary waves receive incident wave energy, they will therefore radiate in an isotropic fashion from thousands of elementary radiation sources at the horizon or edge of an object. Thus, diffraction of electromagnetic waves is the apparent bending of waves as they graze the surface of intervening objects or the earth and is explained by Huygens' principle.

This principle assumes that each wavefront progressing from a transmitter to a receiver consists of an infinite number of secondary sources. Therefore, even in the simple case of transmitting from one point to another, there are an infinite number of paths to consider, with each path originating from a secondary area on the progressing wave front.

Fresnel Interference Zones

A *Fresnel zone* is described as a cylindrical area whose center is the direct or shortest path from the transmitter to the receiver and which is spaced from the center sufficiently to increase the direct path length by ½ wavelength (see Chap. 3, "Fading and Path Clearance").[2]

Fresnel zones are numbered from the center outward in such a way that the first zone is ½ wavelength longer than the direct path, the second zone 1 wavelength longer, the third 1½ wavelengths longer, continuing on to infinity.

The region described as the *first Fresnel zone* will account for nearly one-fourth of the total received energy and should therefore be clear of ob-

---

[1] *Radiation Laboratory Series*, No. 13, McGraw-Hill Book Co., New York, Chap. 6.
[2] The same, Chap. 5.

struction. The radius of the first Fresnel zone at any point along the transmission path is dependent on the frequency of operation as well as the spacing between the transmitting and receiving antennas. It can be found from the formula:

$$R = 13.15 \sqrt{\lambda \frac{D_1 \times D_2}{D_3}} \tag{7}$$

in which:

R = first Fresnel zone radius at any point in the path, in feet
D_1 = distance from transmitter to the point, in miles
D_2 = distance from receiver to the point, in miles
D_3 = distance from transmitter to receiver, in miles
λ = wavelength, in centimeters

Reflection of Microwaves by the Earth's Surface

When a wave strikes the surface of the earth (see Fig. 1-3), it is reflected with an angle of reflection equal to the angle of incidence. The magnitude of the reflected signal will depend on the coefficient of reflection, which was defined previously. The reflection does not actually occur at a point on the surface but from an elliptical area that may be large enough to include several Fresnel zones. The field strength of the two rays at the receiving antenna will be the vector sum of the energy contained in each.

If the angle of incidence at the surface of the earth is small, the reflection will take place with very little change in magnitude. But a reversal of phase will occur irrespective of wave polarization. Under these conditions the two waves at the receiving point, R, will have nearly the same amplitude, but will differ in phase. The average phase of the reflected surface radiation from Z_1 to Z_2, or any adjacent zones, changes by an amount just equal to π since the reflected waves from successive zones are in phase opposition.

While these signals are in opposition they do not completely cancel since the energy level contained in each is not equal. The greatest energy is contributed by the first zone in Fig. 1-3; it is reduced by the summation of the energy in the other zones.[1]

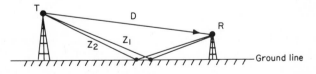

FIG. 1-3.   SURFACE REFLECTION

[1]Radiation Laboratory Series, No. 13, Chap. 5.

2

Microwave Propagation Theory

There are three fundamental ways in which waves may be propagated from the transmitting to the receiving antenna. These are designated as *ground waves, sky waves,* and *space waves.* Analyzing these waves shows that as the frequency of operation is raised above 30 MHz, the ground wave is rapidly attenuated in the atmosphere. Consequently, it has no importance. The sky wave is not effectively refracted back to the earth by the ionosphere at frequencies above 30 MHz but passes right on through. It thus becomes unimportant for ground communications. The space wave, on the other hand, travels directly from the transmitting antenna to the receiving antenna within the earth's troposphere.

The space wave consists of two major components: a ray that travels directly from the transmitting antenna to the receiving antenna, and a ray that is reflected from the surface of the earth or surrounding objects. It is the space wave that is the important mechanism of transmission at microwave frequencies.[1]

Free Space

Free space has been described as the transmission medium when electromagnetic energy is transmitted over a straight line path in a vacuum or an ideal atmosphere, sufficiently removed from all objects that might have any effect on the wave. In this instance, only the direct wave propagated

---

[1]Terman, F. E., *Electronic and Radio Engineering,* McGraw-Hill Book Co., 4th ed., New York, p. 810.

from a transmitting antenna is effective at the receiving antenna. The electric field strength present at any point in the intervening space is called the *free space field strength* (E_o).

Free space field strength depends only upon the effective power transmitted from the antenna and the distance over which the wave is propagated. It may be determined from the following formula:

$$P_R = \frac{G_1 G_2 \lambda^2 P_T}{(4\pi)^2 d^2} \tag{8}$$

in which:

P_R = power at receiving antenna terminals, in watts
P_T = power at transmitting antenna terminals, in watts
G_1 = power gain of transmitting antenna
G_2 = power gain of receiving antenna
d = distance between transmitter and receiver, in meters
λ = wavelength, in meters

This formula assumes proper orientation of the transmitting and receiving antennas and no reflections or refractions so that only the direct path is effective at the receiving antenna.

Propagation Constant

In all mediums that carry wave motion there is a finite velocity at which the wave may travel. This velocity is a function of the composition of the medium itself. The characteristic that defines both the wavelength and dissipation of the electromagnetic field energy is known as the *propagation constant* $(\gamma = \alpha + j\beta)$ and expresses what happens because of energy transfer.[1] The part of the propagation constant that defines the wavelength is known as the *phase constant* (β) and is not fixed, even though the frequency may be constant. The wavelength will vary, however, depending upon the media through which the wave passes.

The part of the propagation constant that describes the dissipation is known as the *attenuation constant*. It explains the loss in amplitude of both the electric and magnetic field vectors.[1] The propagation constant is quite complex in nature and will not be pursued further here.

Atmospheric Transmission

The *troposphere* extends upward from the earth surface to a distance of approximately 6 miles and contains nearly all of the earth's atmosphere. Since the antennas of all point-to-point microwave systems are located

---

[1] *Radiation Laboratory Series*, No. 13, McGraw-Hill Book Co., New York, Chap. 2.

within this region, a knowledge of the transmission effects of waves through the atmosphere is important. For the most part, the troposphere does not have good reflecting ability; the major atmospheric effect is thus due to *refraction* caused by changes in the dielectric constant. However, when an electromagnetic wave encounters a sudden change of large magnitude in dielectric constant, there is a form of reflection called *tropospheric scattering*. This wave is sometimes strong enough to cause interference with the desired transmission.

Microwaves traveling through the lower part of the atmosphere are curved. The curvature is due to the gradual change of refraction index with elevation. Since the refractive index of air depends on its dielectric constant, the temperature, atmospheric pressure, and water vapor content are important. Variation of any of these parameters will have an effect upon the wave propagated through the medium.

A completely homogeneous atmosphere free of sudden changes of temperature, atmospheric pressure, and water vapor will have a refractive index that changes uniformly with elevation. It is called a *standard atmosphere*.

The refractive curving of an electromagnetic wave follows the law of refraction, which says that a ray propagated in a denser medium travels slower than one in a lighter medium.[1] According to this law, a wave propagated in the atmosphere will curve with the earth, tending to place the radio horizon beyond the visible horizon. As both the earth's surface and the radio beam curve, any calculations based on such curves can be simplified by multiplying the earth's radius by some constant that will cause the radio beam to appear as a straight line. As shown in Fig. 2-1, this constant is dependent on the refractive index of the air and has been referred to as K; in a standard atmosphere, it will have a value that is 4/3, or 1.33 times, the actual radius of the earth. The value of K will frequently vary between 0.8 and 3.0, but the value 1.33 is normally found to agree with general atmospheric conditions.

Free Space Attenuation

An *isotropic* attenna in free space theoretically radiates an electromagnetic field evenly in all directions. A wave radiated from such a source spreads out in a spherical form and is called a *spherical wavefront*. As the spherical wavefront expands, the total energy is not dissipated but spreads over an increasingly larger area. Although there is essentially no loss in total energy, there is a decrease in the amount of energy *per square meter* of the wavefront. This decrease in energy between transmitting and receiving antennas is referred to as *free space attenuation*. Because the numbers involved in expressing attenuation of even moderate paths become so large,

---

[1]Terman, F. E., *Electronic and Radio Engineering*, McGraw-Hill Book Co., New York, p. 818.

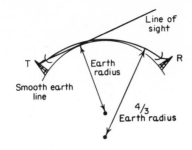

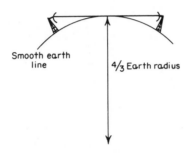

FIG. 2-1.   REFRACTION IN STANDARD ATMOSPHERE

the decibel system is commonly used when referring to *path attenuation.*

The decibel (db) expresses the attenuation in logarithmic form and is equal to 10 times the common logarithm of the power ratio of the transmitted power over the received power:

$$\text{Attenuation (db)} = 10 \, log_{10} \left(\frac{P_T}{P_R} \right) \qquad (9)$$

in which:

P_T = power at transmitter antenna, in watts
P_R = power at receiver antenna, in watts

Since this formula is based solely on atmospheric transmitted power and received power, it can be used with no regard for frequency.

When an electromagnetic wave is propagated through the atmosphere, however, the available power at the receiving antenna is dependent on the *effective area* of the antenna. The following formula then applies:

$$P_R = P \times \text{area} \qquad (10)$$

in which area is expressed in terms of the received wave's wavelength.[1]

---

[1]*Reference Data for Radio Engineers,* 4th ed., IT&T Co., p. 750.

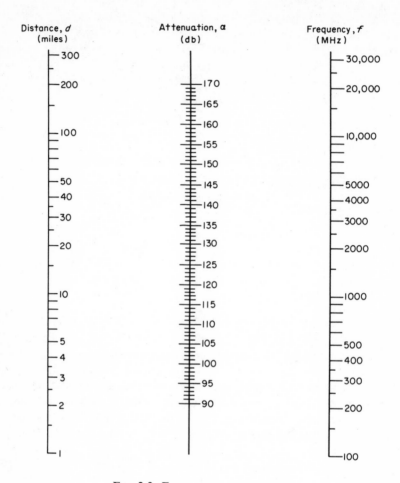

FIG. 2-2. FREE SPACE ATTENUATION

The power radiated is given by the same formula, resulting in a combination of the two:

$$\frac{P_T}{P_R} = \frac{d^2 \lambda^2}{A_T A_R} \tag{11}$$

in which:

A_T = effective area of transmitter antenna
A_R = effective area of receiver antenna
λ = wavelength, in meters
d = distance between antennas, in meters

An *isotropic* radiator is the basic, theoretical form of antenna; it is used as a relative standard for all other antennas. The directivity of any particular microwave antenna compared with this basic form is referred to as *antenna gain*.

The effective area of an isotropic radiator is given by:

$$A = \frac{\lambda^2}{4\pi} \approx 0.8 \ \lambda^2 \qquad (12)$$

It is considered as *unity* gain.

If we assume the same type of antenna at the transmitter and receiver, we can combine the preceding formulas as follows:

$$10 \ log_{10} \left(\frac{P_T}{P_R} \right) = 10 \ log_{10} \ \frac{4.1 \times 10^{12} \ d^2}{G^2 \lambda^2} \qquad (13)$$

in which:

d = distance between antennas, in miles
G = power gain ratio of the antenna over an isotropic radiator
λ = wavelength, in centimeters

This formula is used to express the attenuation between antennas under free space conditions (see Fig. 2-2).

3

Characteristics of Transmission Paths

Since the fundamental mechanism of transmission at microwave frequencies is the space wave, the distance between transmitting and receiving antennas is essentially limited to line-of-sight or optical paths. It therefore becomes very important to avoid any obstacles along the way and to consider the effects of refraction and reflection when engineering the microwave path.

Since complete data covering propagation conditions of a particular path are rarely available, a comprehensive analysis of the transmission characteristics that influence a microwave path can rarely be made. However, it is possible to predict, with a fairly high degree of acuracy, the variations in path loss that will occur under changing meterological conditions. If these effects are carefully considered, and allowances are made for the detrimental effects, highly satisfactory operation can be obtained.

Variations in path loss are normally referenced to a relatively fixed loss that would occur between antennas under a condition of free space transmission. This is referred to as the *mean* or design signal condition. Under these conditions, only the direct wave is effective at the receiving antenna because enough clearance is usually available to prevent the wave from being severely affected by surrounding objects. If propagation conditions remained constant, there would be no concern beyond establishing a satisfactory mean signal. Propagation conditions, however, are rarely ever constant, and nearly all changes and variations of these conditions result in changes in the amplitude of the received wave. These changes are called *fading,* regardless of the cause (whether inverse beam bending, multipath, or out-of-phase reflections).

Fading

As stated, *fading* occurs when the strength of a received signal is reduced for one reason or another. Losses of signal strength that are the result of reflection, and to some extent refraction, can usually be reduced by the proper path engineering. Those which result from meteorological conditions or multipath must either be accepted or handled by proper design of the electronic equipment. With the exception of reducing the mean path loss, or the use of diversity, little can be done from the standpoint of path engineering.

Fading Versus Path Clearance

Understanding the cause of some forms of fading, as well as the requirement for a given amount of path clearance, depends on a clear understanding of the concept of Fresnel zones. Figures 3-1 and 3-2 show how the Fresnel zones surround the direct beam from the transmitting antenna. As can be seen, the energy received at "R" is a summation of the energy in the wavefront. If the shortest distance between "T" and "R" is designated d, then the energy arriving at "R" by paths of greater length than d will be delayed in time or phase. As these paths approach a half wavelength longer, the energy received will be in phase-opposition to the direct wave, and cancellation will

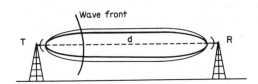

FIG. 3-1. FRESNEL ZONES SURROUNDING THE DIRECT BEAM

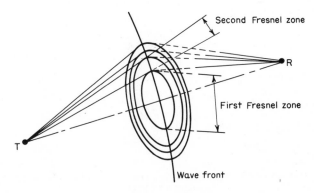

FIG. 3-2. FIRST AND SECOND FRESNEL ZONES

take place. For those paths that approach a full wavelength longer, the energy will arrive in phase, and power addition will take place. If this form of reasoning is continued, energy arriving with a delay of odd half wavelengths will produce cancellation of the direct ray. Conversely, energy arriving with a delay of even half wavelengths will reinforce the direct energy.

The relative effect of these various fields of energy decreases as the indirect path diverges from the direct path. There are two reasons for this phenomenon. The first is the conventional decrease in energy with increased distance. The second is that the face of the wavefront is spherical in nature as it is propagated, and the energy received from any given point on the wavefront will thus have a vector relation to the direct energy. Accordingly, it will have both amplitude and angle (see Fig. 3-3) with reference to the energy received by the direct path. When this energy combines with the direct energy, there will be cancellation or addition depending on the angle, and to a magnitude determined by the amplitude. It is easy to see that, as the angle continues to rotate, the energy received at "R" will approach zero when the angle is 90 deg.

The Fresnel zones, therefore, are determined by the paths that would be followed by the various points on the wavefront. These are added either in phase or exactly out of phase with the field arriving by means of the direct path. For example, the energy traveling a path that will make it arrive 180 deg out of phase with the direct field determines the boundary of the first Fresnel zone. Likewise, energy traveling a path that will make it arrive exactly in phase (360 deg) with the direct field (reinforcement) determines the boundary of the second zone, and so on to any given number of zones (see Fig. 3-2).

Figure 3-4 plots the ratio in decibels between free space transmission and transmission over three theoretical types of terrain for various ratios of actual clearance to first Fresnel zone clearance. As can be seen in the curve

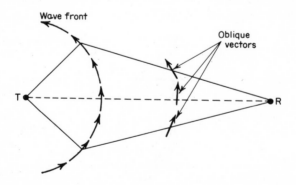

FIG. 3-3.   VECTOR RELATION OF WAVEFRONT ENERGY (ANY POINT) TO
DIRECT ENERGY

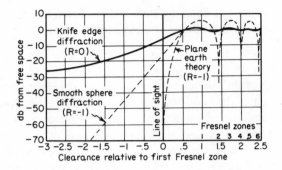

FIG. 3-4. EFFECT OF PATH CLEARANCE ON RADIO WAVE PROPAGATION

labeled *plane earth theory,* a power rise of 6 db is indicated when the positive clearance equals one Fresnel zone. From the previous discussion it was shown that energy delayed by the first Fresnel zone, upon arriving at the receiver, would be in phase opposition with the direct energy arriving at "R." But here we see that this is not the case. The reason is that the beam is rotated 180 deg at the point of reflection and consequently arrives in phase, not in phase opposition, as shown in Fig. 3-5. An explanation of this is as follows.

The behavior of a wave upon striking a reflecting surface may be determined by an adaptation of Huygens' construction. In Fig. 3-5 an electromagnetic wave is shown reflected from a surface somewhere between a transmitting and receiving antenna. This drawing illustrates a wavefront A′B impinging upon a surface of the ground through which it cannot penetrate. If the earth's surface had been absent, the wave would have advanced without change in direction, and in a certain time interval it would have reached the point A′B. However, the presence of the earth's reflecting surface causes a change in the direction of the wavefront, as illustrated by line ACB. The line CB represents the *incidence* wavefront, and the line AC represents the *reflected* wavefront. The angle of incidence and the angle of

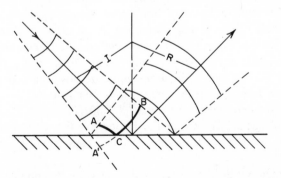

FIG. 3-5. PHASE REVERSAL DUE TO REFLECTION

reflection are equal and lie in the same plane. From this it can be seen that the ray actually rotates 180 deg at the reflection point.

Reflection

The effect of the curvature of the earth, or any obstruction in the radio path, acts to place the receiving antenna in a shadow region if the transmitting and receiving antennas are not within line-of-sight of each other. Where line-of-sight paths are used, the signal level at the receiving antenna is dependent upon both the direct and reflected waves; this level will vary, depending upon frequency and path clearance, and can reach a theoretical maximum of 6 db above the free space value. The change in path loss that may be experienced from *plane earth, smooth sphere,* and *knife-edge diffraction* theory is shown in Fig. 3-4.

In practice, actual paths should normally have characteristics that are between those shown for smooth sphere and knife-edge diffraction, although characteristics that closely approach those of smooth sphere and knife-edge diffraction have been found in actual path tests. Figure 3-4 shows that, depending upon the nature of the interfering surface, when the clearance drops below half the radius of the first Fresnel zone, the received signal falls below the value of free space. Figures 3-6 and 3-7 are nomograms for the calculation of the diameter of the first Fresnel zone.

The curves labeled *plane-earth theory* and *smooth-sphere diffraction* apply to paths that cross highly efficient reflecting surfaces, such as desert or water. Transmission over these efficient reflecting surfaces requires special consideration to combat deep fading. The curve denoted *knife-edge diffraction* applies to the largest portion of paths where communications services are required to operate. These paths are usually free from such atmospheric conditions as excessive fog fronts, temperature inversions, or other severe atmospheric irregularities, and traverse terrain which is moderately to severely rough with brush or wooded covering.

But since every obstacle is different in size, shape, and amount of vegetation, the knife-edge diffraction curve cannot be interpreted exactly. The curve, therefore, is an approximation in the negative clearance region. In the positive clearance region the curve follows the plane-earth or smooth-sphere curves, but does not vary as much from the free space value.

Shadow loss, or loss in the area behind an obstacle, depends upon the frequency. As frequency rises, there is a greater tendency for the waves to follow straight line-of-sight and not to be diffracted into the shadow area behind the obstacle. The lower the frequency, the more diffraction, and therefore the less shadow loss, since stronger signals will be present in the shadow area.

As pointed out in Chap. 1, there will be some loss due to *grazing* if the

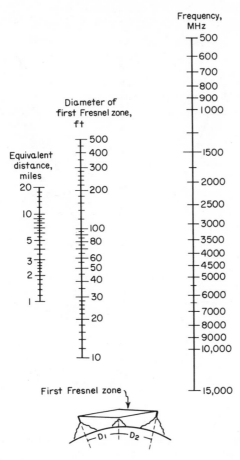

Fig. 3-6. Determination of first Fresnel zone diameter using equivalent distance (see Fig. 3-7) and frequency

antennas of a point-to-point microwave system are low compared to the Fresnel zone clearance required (causing a small angle of incidence) or if there is an obstacle near the line-of-sight path. This loss is shown on the curves in Fig. 3-4. It is the loss present where the various diffraction curves pass the line-of-sight or zero ordinate. Using the knife-edge diffraction curve, for example, the grazing loss would be approximately 6 db; for smooth-sphere the grazing loss would be nearly 15 db.

In general, reflections occur over an area or a number of points along the path. It is necessary to select an antenna height sufficient to prevent the reflected signals from causing nulls under varying propagation conditions. Where strong ground reflections are prevalent — over salt flats, water, or desert paths, for instance — the effects of reflection may be minimized by

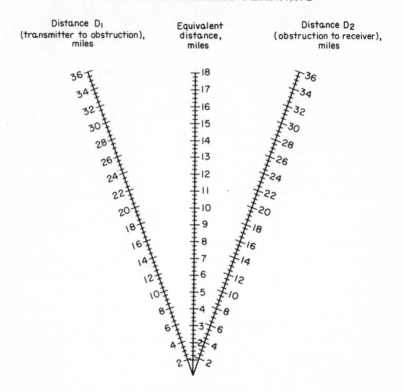

FIG. 3-7. DETERMINATION OF EQUIVALENT DISTANCE FOR FIRST FRESNEL ZONE

providing Fresnel clearances such that, under normal propagation conditions, the received signal level lies in the middle of a broad hump.

Common Terrain Types

The three terrain types specified — knife-edge, smooth spherical surface, and plane earth — will not always fall within any one path. However, these do represent the extremes that will be found in actual practice. All have a different coefficient of reflection.

The *knife-edge* type of terrain assumes the reflection coefficient of the surface to be zero, and consequently, refraction rather than reflection plays an important part in determining the received signal strength. The *smooth-sphere* condition is a modification of the *plane earth* case, and each of these involves both refraction and reflection. As stated previously, if reflection is involved, reinforcement occurs at odd zone clearances and cancellation occurs at even zone clearances. On the paths where the reflection coefficient is low, the nulls and peaks indicated in Fig. 3-4 are reduced in magnitude.

But if a high reflection coefficient surface is involved in the path, serious degradation to the received signal will result from cancellation at the even zone clearance.

Refraction

As shown in Chap. 1, *refraction* is a bending of the radio wave due to changes in the dielectric constant of the atmosphere. The dielectric constant is affected by changes in atmospheric temperature, pressure, and humidity. In a standard atmosphere the index of refraction decreases linearly with height, thus causing the upper portion of the wavefront to travel at a higher velocity than the portion nearer the earth. As a result, the radio wave follows the curvature of the earth, effectively increasing the earth's radius. Under normal propagation conditions this increase is equal to approximately one-third of the earth's radius (see Fig. 2-1). Therefore, it is common to plot the radio path on profile paper that is corrected to four-thirds the earth's radius. Clearances of obstructions are then noted on the profile paper to insure that path clearance is provided.

Since the magnitude of the refraction is a function of the dielectric constant of the air as well as the frequency of the transmitted signal, it is not uncommon in some areas to use a value of curvature different from 4/3 at frequencies above 500 MHz if atmospheric conditions depart substantially from a standard atmosphere.

Variations in the atmosphere occur hourly and daily as well as geographically. In addition, the general condition of the atmosphere is subject to wide seasonal variations that also cause transmission changes. When inversions of temperature occur, the index of refraction increases with height. The microwave beam is then bent away from the earth, producing an effective flattening of the earth's surface. Conversely, the index of refraction may decrease rapidly enough to cause excessive bending of the microwaves toward the earth. Under this latter condition, the earth's surface appears to bulge, reducing the path clearance. The effect of changes such as these on path clearance can be studied by plotting radio path profiles with different effective earth radii.

The change of earth curvature caused by refraction is denoted by the parameter K, which is defined as the ratio between the effective earth radius and the true earth radius:

$$K = \frac{\text{effective earth radius}}{\text{true earth radius}} \tag{14}$$

The vertical distance between flat earth $(K = \infty)$ and the effective earth at any given point can be calculated from the formula:

$$H = D_1 D_2 / 1.5K \tag{15}$$

Where D_1 and D_2 are the distance in miles from a given point to each end of the path, and H is the vertical distance in feet, this formula permits the plotting of any effective earth radius between two points for any value of K so that the microwave ray may be plotted as a straight line.

In addition to homogeneous changes that uniformly vary the dielectric constant of the atmosphere, stratification of hot and cold air masses often causes abrupt changes in the dielectric constant. A radio wave entering such a discontinuous area suffers both refraction and reflection with a consequent change in path loss.

Ducting

Another of the unusual irregularities caused by refraction of radio waves is the phenomenon called *ducting*. Ducts are effective waveguides caused by low altitude, high density atmospheric layers. They occur most frequently near or over large bodies of water and in climates where temperature inversions frequently take place.

An understanding of ducting is readily obtained by analyzing the "M profile."[1] It has become customary for engineers not to refer to the actual refractive index of the air but to a distribution of indices known as the modified refractive index M. This index is defined by the relation:

$$M = \left(\eta - 1 + \frac{h}{a} \right) \times 10^6 \qquad (16)$$

in which:

η = refractive index
h = height above ground
a = radius of earth = 6.37×10^6 m

From this it can be seen that an M-Profile is a graphical cross section of the atmosphere. It shows the changes of the index of refraction with altitude and is drawn by plotting M as abscissa and h as ordinate. Under standard atmospheric conditions, the value of M will be found to increase 0.036 units per foot. The standard M-Profile will therefore be a straight line, as shown in Fig. 3-8a, with a slope of 3.6 per hundred feet. Any path curvatures determined under conditions of standard M-Profile will be found to agree with an effective earth radius equal to 4/3 the acual radius. Figure 3-8a also shows a state known as *substandard,* in which the M-Profile variation is greater than 3.6 per hundred feet. Under these conditions the propagated wave tends to travel in a straight line, resulting in *inverse beam bending.* As will be seen later, weather can play a very important role in changing the dielectric constant of air, thus producing wide variations in the M-Profile.

---

[1] *Radiation Laboratories Series,* No. 13, Sections 1-4, McGraw-Hill Book Co., New York.

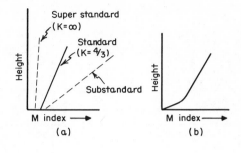

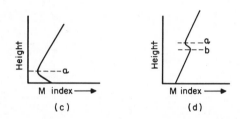

FIG. 3-8.   COMMON M-PROFILES
(a) Standard; (b) substandard surface layer; (c) surface ducting; (d) elevated duct.

Figure 3-8b shows a condition where the substandard state prevails up to a certain elevation and then proceeds at the standard 3.6 units per hundred feet. This condition, called a *surface layer,* frequently results in inverse beam bending up to the point of uniform variation. Figure 3-8c shows a condition in which a substandard *M*-Profile results in a state known as *super standard* (see Fig. 3-8a), but only to a point at which conditions again become normal and the profile returns to the value of 3.6 per hundred feet. This condition produces a very distinct bending of the wave and causes the signal to become trapped between the surface of the earth and the height (represented by point "a"). Most commonly referred to as *surface ducting,* it frequently accompanies strong temperature inversions or a rapid decrease in water vapor.

Still a fourth condition is shown in Fig. 3-8d, which is similar to 3-8c except that it occurs at elevations where the *M*-Profile is also standard above it. This is referred to as an *elevated duct.* It has been known to trap microwaves, causing them to completely miss their target. In this instance the wave is trapped between the points indicated by "a" and "b". When this area takes on a favorable dimension, the wave will be transmitted within the duct in much the same manner as a waveguide.

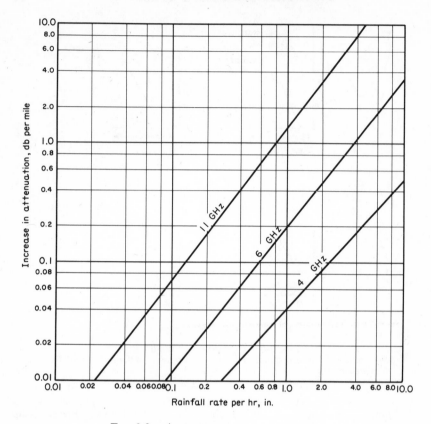

FIG. 3-9.   ATTENUATION DUE TO RAINFALL

Meteorological Irregularities

Fog, another form of meteorological irregularity causing variations in free space loss, is perhaps more common than ducting. The presence of a fog front in a microwave path will tend to refract the signals, increasing the path attenuation. Rain is still another of the meteorological conditions that should be mentioned, and Fig. 3-9 shows a theoretical curve (after Ryde and Ryde) of the increased attenuation due to rainfall. The amount of attenuation indicated for the 6 GHz frequency band should be significant only on problem paths in areas where heavy rainfall is encountered. However, when high propagation reliability is required at frequencies above 10 GHz, rain attenuation should be included in path calculations because the physical size of the rain drops becomes a significant percentage of a wavelength.

4

Transmission Performance

Reliability has two meanings in the microwave communications field. The first is the conventional definition covering the ability of the various pieces of equipment to remain operational for extended periods. The second aspect is that of *transmission reliability,* a measure of propagation characteristics and the ability of properly operating equipment to provide adequate performance under all transmission conditions.

The first form of reliability, that associated with continuous operation of the equipment, can be made to approach 100 per cent by the use of redundant units coupled with extremely fast switching times and can thus be ignored.

Transmission reliability can also be made to approach a very high percentage, although not equal to equipment reliability. It is this second form of reliability, therefore, which will be examined in this chapter.

In making propagation performance reliability calculations, the simplest and safest method is to assume that outages of series links do *not* occur simultaneously. In many applications, the performance standards of industrial microwave systems must be high enough to provide for *toll quality* telephone operation. For this reason, the performance of a microwave system is usually based on the percentage of time that acceptable signal levels are obtained at the radio receiver, rather than system availability.

Toll quality is a term which has come to mean different things to different people but essentially refers to the noise performance of a standard long distance voice circuit. One value accepted as toll quality performance is a

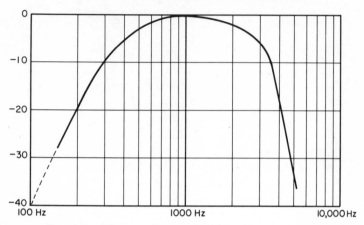

FIG. 4-1. WESTERN ELECTRIC FIA WEIGHTING CURVE

figure of 38 dba measured with a Western Electric FIA weighting network (see Fig. 4-1) on a 4000-mile circuit.[1] This is the total noise contribution from all sources, composed of power hum, receiver noise, modulator noise, intermodulation, and atmospherics, if any. The figure of 38 dba is then divided among the many pieces of electronic hardware so that each section of the total 4000-mile circuit has a particular noise specification. Equipment intermodulation plays an important part in the noise performance, but this is handled in a different manner.

Microwave performance is made continuous by engineering sufficient antenna gain into the installation to overcome all expected fixed and variable losses. The fixed losses are readily accounted for. However, fading, which effectively increases the path loss, is normally predicted on the basis of the maximum loss expected to occur during a specified percentage of the time. This means that a *margin of gain* must be engineered into each hop. This is accomplished by selecting antenna sizes so that anticipated fading will not cause excessive noise or actual outage. *Fade margin* is defined as the amount of gain that is added to the normal system gain in order to allow the facilities to maintain a specified signal-to-noise ratio during the expected fades. The amount of this fade margin will determine the percentage of the time that the microwave signals will be below an acceptable value.

To make effective use of the increased signal strength provided for overcoming fading, the electronic equipment must have sufficient dynamic range to avoid overloading the receiver when the path attenuation reaches a minimum. The wide dynamic range of present day receivers is obtained by incorporating good AGC systems and is usually sufficient to handle changes of path attenuation of 40 to 60 db without fear of overloading.

---

[1]*Reference Data for Radio Engineers*, 4th ed., I.T.&T. Corp., p. 839.

System Engineering

Almost any microwave installation can be engineered to provide acceptable signals. There is, of course, a point at which the cost of additional equipment will not increase the signal-to-noise ratio in any practical proportion. There is also a point at which the outage time of a system could become great enough to make the system nearly useless.

The signal-to-noise (S/N) performance of a microwave installation is actually determined by two criteria. One is the noise contribution of *intermodulation,* which results from the multiplicity of signals that the electronic equipment must handle. The other is the *thermal* or *fluctuation noise,* which is essentially a function of received signal strength. Though their noise contribution is from separate phenomena, they are to some extent interrelated. (The interrelation is discussed further in Chap. 5.)

The S/N performance of a microwave system, consisting of a series of hops, is a function of the S/N performance of *each individual section* of the system. Therefore, from the standpoint of performance, two important decisions must be made before proceeding with the engineering work: (1) Should the signal be allowed to fade out so as to produce a complete interruption, and, if so, how often and for what period of time? (2) What is the minimum acceptable signal-to-noise ratio, and how often and how long can it be tolerated?

The second problem is the more common. One approach to it is to determine the percentage of time that the performance must be above the specified quality for the complete system and then work backward from this figure. For example, if an installation has nine sections, each with a performance reliability of 99.9 per cent, it is safe to estimate that each section will be out a maximum of 0.1 per cent of the time. Assuming that outages will occur at different times, the system will have 0.1×9 or 0.9 per cent maximum outage. This will reduce the over-all system performance reliability to 99 per cent. If this is not satisfactory, it will be necessary to increase the mean signal strength. To do this, fade margin must be added to the mean space loss, and the antenna gains and fixed losses associated with each section must then be adjusted to obtain the required signal-to-noise performance.

Multipath Signals

As the length of the microwave path is increased, the number of possible indirect paths by which the signal may be received increases rapidly. As stated in Chap. 1, the signals from these various indirect paths, when added to the direct signal, cause field strength variations around the median signal value. In most cases the variations will be completely random, resulting in what is sometimes called *Rayleigh fading,* or *Rayleigh distribution signals* (from the law of scattering used by Lord Rayleigh to explain why the sky is blue and applied to any scattering object with small dimensions in terms of wavelength).

Multipath fading is usually plotted as the fraction of the total time that the received signal will be above or below a given median level. (Although this level is actually the RMS value of the variation, it is usually permissible to associate it with the free-space value.) It is handled in this manner because a *Rayleigh distributed signal* represents the random addition of a large number of equal level vectors. (See Fig. 3-3).

Although in multipath fading the actual number of fades per unit of time increases directly with the frequency of operation, total outage time is not related to operating frequency so long as fading is strictly the multipath type. To put it another way, a lower operating frequency can be expected to result in fewer fades of longer duration than a high frequency with many fades of short duration. This is explained as follows: When a constantly changing path difference between direct and indirect paths approaches exactly half a wavelength, cancellation and deep multipath fading can result. This effect will vary with frequency for any given path difference as a result of the difference of wavelength. Although cancellation may occur on a high frequency, it may not be possible to approach a half wavelength at lower frequencies. From this reasoning, it can be seen that a given path at 960 MHz might be reasonably stable, whereas a 6000 MHz signal on the same path could be receiving multipath fading. (This is the same phenomenon by which *frequency diversity* reduces the effect of fading.) Experience to date at frequencies above 890 MHz has shown that all paths over 25 miles long may be considered as prospects for multipath fading without regard to the frequency of operation.

Multipath Fade Margin

Fading from multipath scattering on paths greater than 25 miles is most pronounced during the summer months, that is, July to October, but varies, of course, with the particular geographic location. Figure 4-2 is a curve based upon the Rayleigh scattering law that can be used to determine how much the desired signal strength must be exceeded to prevent excessive multipath fading.

When using this curve to predict the performance desired for each section, add the indicated excess signal level to each operating path. For example, if the microwave receiver threshold is −85 dbm, and it is desired to have the signal arrive above this level 99 per cent of the time, the received signal must be approximately 18 db above the threshold value, or −67 dbm, in order to provide sufficient signal margin.

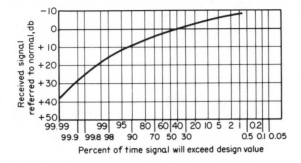

FIG. 4-2. FADE MARGIN BASED ON RAYLEIGH SCATTERING

The performance to be expected from a typical microwave installation used for multichannel telephone service is plotted in percentage of outage time in Fig. 4-3. The 100 channel miles referred to in the curve means 100 miles of two-way transmission. (The figure of 100 is chosen as a means of providing a common denominator for the various systems available.) The curves shown represent the pérformance that can be expected for any particular fading margin. The improved performance of frequency diversity is also shown for three conditions of separation of the RF channel.

If the conditions of adequate clearance have been met and the fading is strictly of a Rayleigh nature, the performance curves shown are applicable to microwave systems operating on frequencies from 900 to 11,000 MHz and paths from 15 to 100 miles in length. In those areas where heavy rainfall is expected during certain periods of the year, attenuation on higher frequencies due to rainfall should be considered in addition to the margins of operations shown in Fig. 4-3. The added attenuation due to rainfall should be included in any calculations of path loss, thus increasing the mean signal level and fade margin. Since this additional margin can be quite costly, the system performance criteria under the worst signal conditions should be carefully analyzed.

Beam Bending

As shown in Chap. 3, beamed microwave signals are influenced by the change of the dielectric constant of the air. The *M*-Profile, as previously described, is a graphical cross-section of the atmosphere showing the change of refraction index with altitude. When the field strength at the receiving antenna is calculated on the basis of a standard *M*-Profile, the curvature of the microwave beam will be found to be four-thirds the earth's actual radius. As mentioned earlier, this is what is referred to as a standard atmosphere.

Though the beam is actually curved under standard conditions, it is considered to be a standard curvature and, therefore, may be considered to be

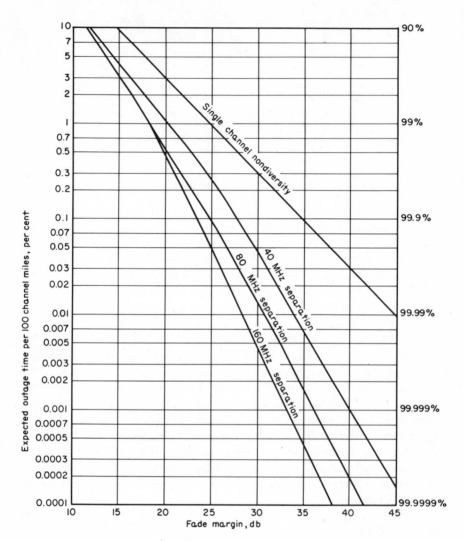

FIG. 4-3.   DIVERSITY ADVANTAGE CURVE
Outage time is due to all types of fading. It is assumed that adequate path clearance exists.

a straight line. The transmitting and receiving antennas are placed so that under these conditions the receiving antenna will intercept the curved beam and the field strength at the receiving antenna will be normal. When the refraction index of the atmosphere is different from that of the standard *M*-Profile, the beam will be bent; under some conditions it may actually miss the receiving antenna, as shown in Fig. 4-4, resulting in severe fading.

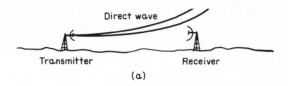

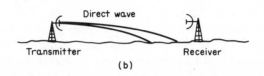

FIG. 4-4.   BEAM BENDING
(a) Inverse bending, substandard index; (b) positive bending, super standard index.

Diurnal Signal Variations

Assuming there is no significant obstruction of the transmission path (first Fresnel zone clearance), steady transmission will occur when the atmosphere is homogeneous, or well mixed. Space loss can be said to be median under these conditions.

When temperatures become irregular and water vapor pressures near the ground cause increases in the *M*-Profile, signal level variations will occur. A change in signal level will invariably accompany this condition on non-optical paths because of multipath fading. But on optical paths the change in signal level is more diurnal in nature, which indicates that fading is of the beam bending variety. Generally, it will be found that a *diurnal signal* will change from a steady state condition at mid-day to a pronounced fade at night. This fading is most pronounced shortly after sundown and shortly after sunrise as a result of the changing conditions of the atmosphere during these periods. *Diurnal fading* is substantially more pronounced in summer than in winter because the air has a higher water content at this time. The higher humidity condition increases the effectiveness of temperature gradients in producing strong *M*-gradients. Diurnal fading is a condition of beam bending, brought on by changes in *M* gradients. These changes also occur frequently during or after the passage of storm fronts. Since these fronts are usually attended by high winds, they can be mistaken for multipath fading, a confusion that can lead to the wrong corrective action. If the fading is compared with the passage of frontal systems and the rising and setting of the sun, however, an approximate relationship can be established to distinguish one from the other. Any hard and fast statements may be misleading since exceptions occur as a result of seasonal effects or combinations of weather changes, and a clear cut case is seldom found.

Fading Compensation

The usual procedure for handling fading, as shown previously, is to increase the fade margin. This can be accomplished in three ways. The first is to increase the antenna gain by making the antenna larger. The second is to reduce the path loss by decreasing the transmitter-to-receiver separation. The third is to increase the power of the transmitter. The effects of these vary widely and, in some instances, can actually aggravate the problem.

When fade margin is increased by increasing antenna gain, the gain is obtained by decreasing the beamwidth of the propagated signal. This is a satisfactory method of correcting a fading due to multipath, but if the fading is a result of beam bending the reduced beam width may be bent far enough to miss the receiving antenna completely. The second approach, that of reducing transmitter-receiver separation, is most effective on nonoptical paths. However, the amount by which the path must be reduced to obtain adequate fade margin is usually too great to make it practical. The same can be said of the third method of obtaining fade margin; the amount of power increase must be very large if fade margin is obtained solely in this manner.

The most effective means of obtaining greater fade margin is, of course, a compromise among all three methods.

Diversity Systems

When the engineering to improve the inherent performance of the equipment has been carried to a point of diminishing returns, and a satisfactory performance is still impossible, *diversity operation* may be the answer.

Diversity operation is described as the simultaneous operation of two or more systems. It takes two forms: one is known as *frequency diversity,* in which the same information is transmitted on two or more separate radio frequencies at the same time. The other is *space diversity,* in which the receiver is designed to have multiple sections, and each section is connected to an individual antenna. The antennas are separated far enough to provide at least a half wavelength between the geometrical path difference of two signals received from the transmitter.

Frequency Diversity

For reasons that were explained in the preceding paragraphs, signals at different frequencies fade at different rates. Experience has shown that when two signals separated by as little as 100 MHz are received, any fading present on the two signals will be completely incoherent. This can be seen graphically from the curves of Fig. 4-3, which show the reduction of fade margin possible with increased order of diversity. When paths are engineered to provide a particular fade margin, performance will improve quite rapidly as the order of diversity is increased.

In *frequency diversity systems,* the information to be transmitted is usually applied to two or more separate transmitting units that operate on spaced frequencies. The receivers are connected to a *diversity combiner,* the function of which is to accept baseband information from the units simultaneously and to select the best of the group.

Space Diversity

In *space diversity systems* two or more antennas are spaced several wavelengths apart, usually vertically. Experience has shown that when fading does occur, it will rarely be the same on both antennas at the same time. This is true of multipath fading only. Diurnal fading, or inverse beam bending, however, will usually reduce the signal on both antennas simultaneously unless very large separations are used. In most cases, nevertheless, sufficient output is available from one or the other of the antennas to provide a useful signal for the receiver.

Placing the antennas at different heights is a convenient means of compensating for the different path lengths between the direct and reflected waves. As can be seen from the information of Fresnel zones, it is possible to have a reflected signal reinforce a direct signal at different positions in space. This is the phenomenon on which space diversity usually depends.

The combining procedure for space diversity is the same as for frequency diversity.

Design Objectives

Variations in received signal level, or fading, in a microwave system cannot be predicted with absolute accuracy. But over the years many observations have been made of the behavior of existing microwave systems. From these observations some of the characteristics of fading have been studied and, as a result, it is now possible to plan microwave systems that will provide reliable performance. It has been determined that two types of fading are the most prevalent: (1) inverse beam bending and (2) Rayleigh or multipath. As explained previously, the first is caused by atmospheric conditions changing the refraction index, and the second is the result of interference between two or more signals, or rays, traveling over slightly different routes through the atmosphere.

Propagation conditions	Perfect	Good	Average	Poor	Very poor
Weather	Standard atmosphere	No temperature inversion or fog	Some sub-standard light fog	Surface layers and ground fog	Ducting-fog and over water
Geographic location		Rocky Mountains	Plain states and Northeast	Coastal	Coastal and Gulf states
60-85 performance reliability			0.6F K=4/3	1.0F K=4/3	0.6F K=1
85-98 performance reliability		0.6F K=4/3	1.0F K=4/3	0.6F K=1	0.3F K=2/3
98-99.9 performance reliability	0.6F K=4/3	1.0F K=4/3	0.6F K=1	0.3F K=2/3	Grazing K=1/2
99.9-99.99 performance reliability	1.0F K=4/3	0.6F K=1	0.3F K=2/3	Grazing K=1/2	Grazing K=5/12

FIG. 4-5. PATH CLEARANCE CRITERIA (F = FIRST FRESNEL ZONE)

Performance reduction due to fading can be controlled by proper equipment engineering if proper path clearance has been obtained. Figure 4-5 is a table of generally accepted path clearance criteria. The performance reliability figures shown are the percentage of time the received signal will be at or above the design median. This table will be helpful in determining proper antenna heights for the various values of K so that the necessary clearances may be obtained.

Microwave systems which are intended to carry only voice communication can be designed for a somewhat reduced standard of performance unless they are interconnected with automatic dial exchanges. For commercial telephone applications, TV broadcasting, or data transmission, the minimum over-all system performance should be on the order of 99 per cent to avoid undue loss or repetition of transmitted information. A 99 per cent system will be unusable 1 per cent of the time, or a total of 88 hours during the year for a full-time system. On a properly engineered installation with diversity or stand-by equipment, this time is usually divided into short periods of outage due to switching or fast fades, as well as down-time for maintenance.

A much more satisfactory figure for propagation reliability, and one that is commonly used by most of the telephone companies in the United States, is 99.9 per cent for the complete system. This frequently means that for a multihop system a performance reliability of 99.99 per cent must be obtained for each hop. In a ten-hop system this would mean that each individual hop will be operable for all but 53 minutes of the year, as shown in Fig. 4-6.

Propagation reliability, per cent	Outage time, per cent	Outage time		
		Yearly	Monthly average	Daily average
0	100	8760 hrs	720 hrs	24 hrs
50	50	4380 hrs	360 hrs	12 hrs
80	20	1752 hrs	144 hrs	4.8 hrs
90	10	876 hrs	72 hrs	2.4 hrs
95	5	438 hrs	36 hrs	1.2 hrs
99	1	88 hrs	7 hrs	14 min
99.9	0.1	8.8 hrs	43 min	1.4 min
99.99	0.01	53 min	4.3 min	8.6 sec
99.999	0.001	5.3 min	26 sec	0.86 sec

FIG. 4-6. SYSTEM RELIABILITY TIME

5

Microwave System Performance

In the course of planning and engineering a microwave installation, it is easy to overlook the fundamental purpose of the system, which is to provide dependable, interference-free communication. Once all the requirements of selecting sites and antenna sizes have been completed, some questions still remain: How well will the system perform? How much of the time can it be used?

There are many factors to be considered in planning a dependable system. These will take on different emphasis depending on the type of system. Continuity of operation can be made to approach 100 per cent by providing hot stand-by, continuous power, or battery operation. Under these conditions, coupled with extremely fast switching times, the actual outage can be very small.

The performance of a microwave system depends not only on continuity but also on noise-free operation and the general performance characteristics that apply to all systems. The systems in use today employ various modulation techniques that strongly influence the noise and interference performance of the equipment. Since most of the systems in service are FM systems, this chapter will emphasize FM operation.

Interference — General

In addition to desired radio signals, almost any sensitive receiving system picks up noises of various types. Much of this noise is a result of voltages induced in the receiver input circuits from either natural or man-made sources. Its magnitude in the presence of the desired signal determines the quality of the communication provided by the facility.

The noise is troublesome from the standpoint of its interference effect as well as its desensitization effect on the receiver. Man-made noises are those that arise from electrical devices and, for this reason, are particularly present in cities and areas of heavy industrial activity. Noises from natural sources are often referred to as *static*. At the lower microwave frequencies, *solar noise* and *galactic noise* become important. (Solar noise comes from the earth's sun, whereas galactic noise originates in the stars.)

Disturbances that are occasional and relatively infrequent are referred to as *impulse* noise. This type of noise is usually an explosive type pulse from atmospheric disturbances such as lightning or from a man-made source such as ignition systems. If the noise pulses occur so frequently that they overlap, producing continuous noises that are not clearly separated, the noise is referred to as *random noise*. Tube and thermal fluctuations are examples of random noise, as are solar and galactic noise.

Random noise, when a result of thermal fluctuations or other circuit influences, is usually found to have a uniform amplitude with a fixed deviation. It contains all frequencies from zero to infinity. Random noises from most other sources tend to have broad frequency peaking effects that center themselves in certain areas of the radio spectrum (see Fig. 5-1).

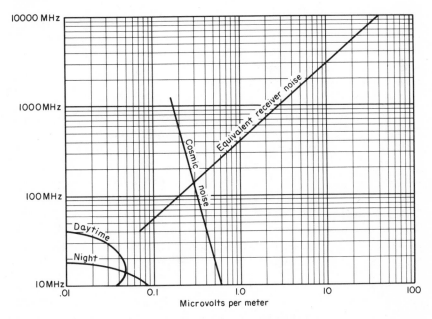

FIG. 5-1. RADIO NOISE DISTRIBUTION

Atmospheric Interference

The interference normally called *static* is fundamentally a radio signal, with frequency components spread over a wide spectrum. The noise is propagated in the same manner as ordinary radio signals of the same frequency. For this reason, at the lower microwave frequencies, the noise received at any particular point is the sum of near-by noise and noise from a distance which is propagated to the receiving equipment. The noise generator may be lightning or another type of electrical discharge. With the exception of thunderstorms, noise will usually follow seasonal variations of wave propagation; its intensity will vary accordingly.

Most noise of this type is confined to the lower portion of the microwave spectrum, as can be seen in Fig. 5-1. The higher end of the spectrum is relatively unaffected because the higher frequency components on the flashes are not effectively reflected by the ionosphere. Also, natural electrical discharges generate relatively small amounts of radio energy at ultra and super high frequencies. For the above reasons, it will be found that variations in noise intensity are approximately inversely proportional to the square of the operating frequency, and the absolute noise level is proportional to the square root of the bandwidth.

Solar and Cosmic or Galactic Noise

The earth is constantly influenced by radio frequency radiation of extraterrestrial origin in the form of noise. The sources of cosmic (galactic) noise are continuously distributed throughout our galaxy, with a few point sources having very high intensities. When a microwave antenna happens to be pointed at one of these points, the noise output of a sensitive receiving system will usually be influenced by it.

The intensity of these radiations at the surface of the earth varies with frequency. It is usually greater as the frequency is reduced, up to the point where ionospheric penetration is not possible. Little can be done to avoid pointing an antenna at these points of high radiation because nearly every area of the sky will fall within the antenna pattern as the earth sweeps through its annual cycle. Therefore, the microwave signal intercepted by a receiving antenna must have a field intensity greater than that of the *site noise* in order to be usable. The required field intensity necessary in the presence of galactic noise is expressed approximately by the formula:

$$E = 2/\sqrt{f} \tag{17}$$

in which:

E = microvolts per meter

f = operating frequency, in MHz (for frequencies between 18 and 160 MHz)

At frequencies above 160 MHz the field intensity of cosmic noise is extremely small and usually can be disregarded. The sun also contributes a substantial amount of noise, particularly when a microwave antenna is pointed directly at it late in the afternoon or early in the morning.

The theory of thermal radiation predicts that any black body will radiate energy of a certain magnitude at all wavelengths.[1] If this theory is applied to the sun, assuming a temperature of 6000 degrees absolute, the intensity of the noise at 200 MHz will be below the threshold of most present-day receiving systems. On the other hand, the intensities which have been measured at frequencies around 200 MHz correspond to temperatures of nearly a million degrees Kelvin. Also, at times of high sun spot activity, radiation intensities corresponding to a billion degrees Kelvin have been observed.

Solar noise measurements made at frequencies of 3 to 24 GHz have shown definite evidence of radio noise. The intensity of this noise, however, corresponded favorably with that which would be expected from thermal radiation as predicted by Planck's theorem.

Experience has shown that, at times of high sunspot activity, solar noise may be of sufficient magnitude to be noticeable on VHF systems that have high gain antennas pointing directly at the sun. Otherwise the noise is low enough so that special consideration need not be given to this problem on point-to-point systems.

Man-Made Noise

Electrical interference from sources other than natural phenomena is classified as man-made. It is usually generated by electrical devices which may or may not be in perfect working order. For example, power line discharges, motor brush sparking, ignition systems and relays with sparking contacts are likely sources of man-made interferences.

Man-made noise is generally confined to the lower microwave frequencies and almost always is of an impulse nature. Home appliances are another group of devices that contribute to this type of interference.

The field intensity of this type of man-made noise is greatest in populated areas and around industrial installations. The noise is much like normal random noise in that the peak intensity increases as the bandwidth of the receiving system is made larger.

Although interference from man-made noise is normally not significant at the upper microwave frequencies, it has been known to have caused in-

---

[1]Schwartz, *Information Transmission Modulation and Noise*, McGraw-Hill Book Co., p. 278.

tolerable interference at times. For example, some microwave installations have had to be moved because of excessive noise from elevator machinery located in the upper stories of buildings.

Receiver Noise

The noise figure of a receiver is a measure of the extent to which the S/N ratio at the output of a receiver is greater than the S/N ratio at the output of a *perfect* receiver of the same gain and bandwidth. In other words, it is a measure of the noise *added* to a received signal by the receiver itself.

The noise figure determines the smallest signal power which may be received for any particular bandwidth without the signal being obscured by the noise. It represents the most important single characteristic of microwave receivers and is determined from the following equation:

$$\text{NF} = \frac{\text{S/N power ratio of ideal receiver}}{\text{S/N power ratio of actual receiver}} \qquad (18)$$

There are two important contributors to the noise in the output of the receiver:

1. Thermal noise generated by the resistance that the antenna system presents to the receiver input terminals.
2. Noise generated within the receiver by circuit (thermal) and tube noises.

With respect to noise, the part of a receiver between the antenna and the output of the IF amplifier can be considered nothing more than a bandpass amplifier. The fact that the mixer of a receiver changes the frequency of operation does not really alter this view because it simply causes output noise to fall in a different part of the frequency spectrum.

Random noise from thermal agitation is always present to some degree in even the most carefully designed and constructed receivers. When amplified sufficiently, these noises produce a strong high frequency hiss in telephone channels and loudspeakers. In oscilloscope presentations they appear as *grass;* in TV pictures, as *snow.*

The irregular motion of electrons in any resistor and in the space current of vacuum tubes produces *fluctuation noise.* These fluctuations of voltages and currents are completely random but obey the laws of probability. There is a certain probability that the value of voltage or current will be at any one particular value, and at the same time the probability that a very large value will occur is very small. But the probability of a large noise amplitude being present increases as the bandwidth is made larger. Therefore, although the noise fluctuations have no particular waveform, they do

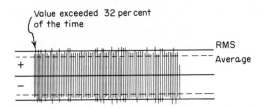

Fig. 5-2. Distribution of Noise Energy

have a definite RMS value and a definite average value for all positive and negative noise amplitudes. The average positive or negative values are equal and make up 80 per cent of the RMS value, whereas instantaneous amplitudes exceed the RMS value nearly 32 per cent of the time, as shown in Fig. 5-2. The noise produced in this manner by fluctuations of voltage and current in the stages of a receiver establishes the limit of amplification that can be used to raise a received signal to a usable value. To phrase it another way, *it is fluctuation noise that limits the sensitivity of a microwave receiver.*

An important quantity associated with fluctuation noise is the available noise power output from any source. The available noise power that can be delivered is obtained by matching a resistive load to the circuit in which the noise is generated. Since fluctuation noise has a uniform spectral density, the available noise power can be calculated without regard to absolute frequency from this formula:

$$E^2 = 4R \times KT \, \Delta f \tag{19}$$

in which:

E = root mean square noise voltage
R = resistance, in ohms
K = Boltzmann's constant (1.38×10^{-23} joules/degree Kelvin)
T = aboslute temperature, in degrees Kelvin
f = bandwidth, in Hertz

In a simpler form, this formula is reduced to:

$$P = 1.38 \times 10^{-11} \, BT \tag{20}$$

in which:

P = power, in microwatts
B = bandwidth, in Hertz
T = temperature, in degrees Kelvin

Noise Figure

Equation 20 gives the magnitude of the noise that is presented to the receiver input stages from the antenna. This noise is not the only noise present in the output of a receiver; each of the stages of a receiver contributes some noise power to the total.

The noise figure of a receiving system can be found as follows:

$$NF = \frac{P_{n\text{-out}}/P_{n\text{-in}}}{P_{s\text{-out}}/P_{s\text{-in}}} \tag{21}$$

in which:

$P_{n\text{-out}}$ = noise power at the stage or receiver output
$P_{n\text{-in}}$ = noise power available from Eq. 20 or the preceding stage
$P_{s\text{-out}}$ = power of the signal at the stage or receiver output
$P_{s\text{-in}}$ = power of the signal preceding the stage or antenna

This calculation can be taken stage by stage, or it can be a composite calculation covering the complete receiver. It is frequently important to isolate a particular stage's noise figure; obviously, a stage-by-stage calculation must be made to determine this.

The noise figure of the complete receiver can be obtained from a summation of the noise contribution of each stage, as follows:

$$NF = F_1 + \frac{(F_2 - 1)}{G_1} + \frac{(F_3 - 1)}{G_1 G_2} + \ldots \frac{(F_n - 1)}{G_n} \tag{22}$$

in which:

NF = noise figure of the combination
F_1 = noise figure of first stage
F_2 = noise figure of second stage
F_3 = noise figure of third stage
F_n = noise figure of nth stage
G_1 = power gain of first stage
G_2 = power gain of second stage
G_n = power gain of nth stage

All quantities are expressed as pure ratios.

In all practical cases of receivers that have been properly designed, the series of Eq. 22 rapidly converges so that only two terms are usually significant. This is true because the second term of the equation has a gain term in the denominator from the first amplifier. Therefore, if the gain of the first stage is large, any source of noise in succeeding stages will have little effect on the noise figure of the combination.

Equation 22 will result in a value that was described earlier in a general manner by Eq. 18 and more pointedly by Eq. 21. This figure is a ratio. It means that any input signal-to-noise ratio will be degraded by a numerical value equal to the receiver noise figure. For example, if a receiver has a signal present at its input which is 20 db above the available power from

Eq. 20, it is said to have a 20 db signal-to-noise ratio. If this signal is passed through a receiver which has a noise figure of 10 db, the output signal-to-noise ratio of the receiver will be 20 db minus 10 db NF, or only a 10 db S/N ratio. *(Note:* This is not a normal power addition but a simple addition of ratios.)

As seen from the above, the *noise figure* of a microwave receiver is a characteristic that places a limit of sensitivity on the receiver and is not influenced by modulation or type of signal transmitted.

Modulation Characteristics

Modulation is defined as the process or the result of the process whereby some characteristic of one wave is made to change in accordance with another wave.[1] There are two main parameters which are varied to transmit information — amplitude and frequency — and there are several different methods of accomplishing the variation.

In *amplitude modulation* (AM), the modulating wave is used to vary the amplitude of the transmitted signal, which may be in the form of ordinary speech, pulses from binary circuits, or simply the result of turning the carrier off and on, as is common for transmission of the Morse code.[2]

Frequency modulation (FM), sometimes called *angle modulation,* is accomplished by changing the frequency around a particular mean frequency in accord with the modulating wave.

Amplitude Modulation

AM modulation is perhaps the oldest and most familiar form of modulation. An example of an AM modulated wave is illustrated in Fig. 5-3. The degree of modulation of a particular wave can be determined from the relation:

$$\text{Positive peak} + M = \frac{E_2 - E_1}{E_1} \tag{23a}$$

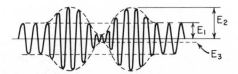

FIG. 5-3. AMPLITUDE MODULATED WAVE

[1]"IRE Standards on Modulation Terms," *Proceedings of the IRE,* May 1953.
[2]For a detailed discussion of AM modulation, see Black, Harold S., *Modulation Theory,* D. Van Nostrand, Co.

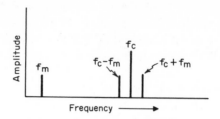

FIG. 5-4. SPECTRUM OF AM WAVE

$$\text{Negative peak} - M = \frac{E_1 - E_3}{E_1} \qquad (23b)$$

in which E_1, E_2, and E_3 are the average carrier, maximum carrier, and minimum carrier, respectively, as indicated in Fig. 5-3.

The spectrum of a modulated carrier is shown in Fig. 5-4 where the three components together represent a double sideband AM carrier. This figure shows how the amplitude variation of the carrier produces sum and difference products called *sidebands*. It is apparent that the width of the frequency spectrum occupied by an AM wave is twice the highest frequency contained in the modulating wave and that it will increase at twice the rate the modulating frequency increases.

The bandwidth that must be transmitted for any particular type of modulating wave will depend on the type of communication involved. It is relatively narrow for the transmission of telegraph signals and very large for television, for instance.

Because all the information contained in the modulating wave is available in both sidebands, there is a substantial waste of signal spectrum when both sidebands are transmitted. Since it is the variation in amplitude of the modulating wave that contains the information, and since these variations appear equally in each sideband, it is reasonable to suggest that transmission of both sidebands is unnecessary and that the elimination of one would halve the required transmission bandwidth. With no message information in the carrier, it too can be eliminated in so far as transmission of the original message information is concerned. (A carrier is necessary for demodulation and recovery of the message, however.)

This method of transmission is referred to as *single sideband suppressed carrier* because the only portion of the modulated carrier transmitted is *one* of the information carrying sidebands. This technique makes it convenient to transmit large amounts of information using a minimum of information bandwidth.

Although AM systems, particularly single sideband systems, are efficient in the use of transmission bandwidth, they offer little possibility for improving the S/N performance of a system. Any noise present in the band of frequencies occupied by an AM signal will be passed through the receiver directly. Accordingly, AM systems are commonly used as a standard of comparison when considering noise performance improvements.

Frequency Modulation

Frequency modulation, on the other hand, offers a simple and effective means of trading bandwidth for noise performance. A frequency modulated wave is defined as one in which the instantaneous frequency of the carrier wave is varied in accordance with the modulating signal while the amplitude of the carrier wave is kept constant. This technique results in a deviation of the carrier frequency, referred to as Δf, around a fixed value, referred to as f_o. (See Fig. 5-5.)

The amount of *frequency deviation* is proportional to the amplitude of the modulating voltage. The rate at which the deviation occurs is proportional to the frequency of the modulating voltage. The magnitude of deviation must be defined because the instantaneous deviation of the carrier frequency is independent of the modulating frequency but proportional to the instantaneous amplitude. The peak instantaneous deviation is thus a measure of the degree to which the carrier is modulated; it is referred to as the *modulation index* (MI).

The modulation index bears an important relationship to the operation of FM systems. It is determined as follows:

$$\text{Modulation index} = \frac{\text{frequency deviation}}{\text{modulating frequency}}$$

or

$$\text{MI} = \Delta f / f_m \qquad (24)$$

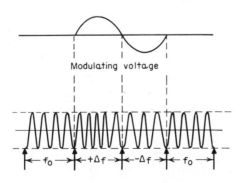

FIG. 5-5. FREQUENCY MODULATED WAVE
Instantaneous frequency changes in accordance with the modulating voltage.

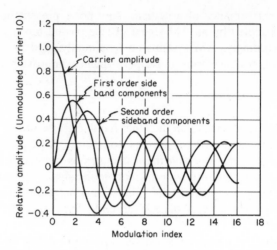

FIG. 5-6.   RELATIVE AMPLITUDE OF FM SIDEBAND COMPONENTS
*The amplitudes shown are for the first and second order sideband
components, relative to the carrier and taken individually, not as a pair.*

The modulation index is also an indication of how much of the carrier
power has been translated into sideband energy. Analysis will show that the
distorted carrier resulting from a sinusoidal modulating frequency is made
up of frequency components spaced in multiples of the modulating frequency.
For example, if a carrier is modulated by a single frequency signal of 1000
Hz, there will be one or more sidebands set up on each side of the carrier
frequency. Each sideband will be separated by 1000 Hz from the carrier and
from each other. From this it can be seen that an FM wave not only has the
same frequency components as an AM wave transmitting the same modulating frequency but also has higher order sidebands.

The amplitude and usable number of frequency components for a sinusoidal modulating signal depend on the modulation index. The amplitude
can be obtained from Fig. 5-6 or calculated with the aid of a table of Bessel
functions.

The characteristics of an FM modulated wave are shown in panoramic
form in Fig. 5-7. As can be seen from this figure, when the modulation index
is held below 0.5, the second and higher order sidebands have very little
energy, and the frequency band required to transmit the FM signal is the
same as for an AM signal. But when the modulation index exceeds 1.0,
there are higher order sidebands of significance that must be accommodated
in order to avoid unnecessary distortion during the demodulation process.
Under these conditions, the bandwidth of an FM wave will be substantially
greater than that required by an AM signal.

A common rule used by microwave engineers is: *An FM-wave contains
sidebands of significance on both sides of the carrier over a frequency spec-*

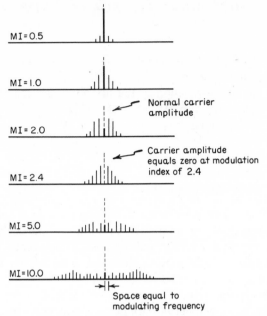

MI = 0.5

MI = 1.0

Normal carrier
amplitude

MI = 2.0

Carrier amplitude
equals zero at modulation
index of 2.4

MI = 2.4

MI = 5.0

MI = 10.0

Space equal to
modulating frequency

FIG. 5-7. FREQUENCY SPECTRUM OF FM WAVE FOR VARIOUS
MODULATION INDEX VALUES

tum equal to the sum of the frequency deviation plus the highest modulating frequency. From this rule, a common bandwidth formula is evolved:

$$BW = 2\Delta f + 2 F_m + d \qquad (25)$$

in which:

BW = bandwidth
Δf = frequency deviation
F_m = highest modulating frequency
d = drift of the carrier

All frequency values are in the same units.

Figure 5-7 shows graphically how the carrier power is translated into the sidebands. In fact, when the intensity of the modulating frequency reaches a value that produces an index of 2.4, the carrier power dips to zero and is converted to sideband energy.

The energy of the various components of an FM wave can be determined by expanding the trignometric formula for the sum of two angles and evaluating the resulting expression. This results in:

$$
\begin{aligned}
e = \; & A J_0 \text{ (MI) } \sin \omega cT \\
& + J_1 \text{ (MI) } [sin \, (\omega cT + \omega M)T - sin \, (\omega c - \omega M)T] \\
& + J_2 \text{ (MI) } [sin \, (\omega c + 2\omega M)T + sin \, (\omega c - 2\omega M)T] \qquad (26) \\
& + J_3 \text{ (MI) } [sin \, (\omega c + 3 \, \omega M)T - sin \, (\omega c - 3\omega M)T] \\
& + J_n \text{ (MI) } \ldots.
\end{aligned}
$$

in which:

e = instantaneous amplitude
A = peak amplitude
J_n (MI) = the Bessel function of the first kind and the "nth" order, in agreement with MI
MI = modulation index
ω = $2\pi f$
c = carrier wave
T = time
M = modulating frequency

While this is a somewhat ominous looking formula, it simply says that to obtain the power of the composite wave for any particular modulation index (MI), you must add algebraically the instantaneous energy of the carrier to the energy of the various sidebands available for any particular modulation index.

When the components of a frequency modulated wave are passed through a frequency multiplier or harmonic generator, the modulation index is increased by a factor equal to the multiplication factor involved. Furthermore, when an FM wave is passed through a frequency divider, the modulation index will be reduced by a factor equal to the division. Thus, the frequency components contained in the wave, and consequently the bandwidth of the wave, will be increased or decreased, respectively, by frequency multiplication or frequency division. (No distortion of the modulation is introduced, however, by the frequency change.) Conversely, when an FM wave is translated in frequency by heterodyning the signal with an oscillator, as in the mixer of a superheterodyne receiver, the modulation index is moved in frequency but otherwise unaltered. Again, the translation process will have no effect on modulation if all sidebands of significance are passed.

Phase Modulation

Another form of frequency modulation is obtained by varying the phase reference so that its magnitude is proportional to the instantaneous amplitude of the modulating signal. If we consider a modulating voltage of the form, $f_m = \omega_m/2\,\pi$, we will obtain:

$$\theta = \theta_o + \text{mp } sin\ \omega_{mt} \qquad (27)$$

in which:

θ = angular position
θ_o = phase in the absence of modulation
mp = phase modulation index
ω_{mt} = 2π times modulation frequency at time t

The *phase modulation* index is the maximum value of the phase change introduced by the modulation.

If the various mathematical formulas for phase modulation are compared with the formulas for frequency modulation, it will be found that when the modulation indexes for the two methods are the same, the relative amplitudes of the various wave components will also be the same. Consequently, the only essential difference between a phase modulated signal and a frequency modulated signal is the manner in which the modulation index is obtained.

There is one other fundamental difference between the two modulation methods that application engineers might note, although its greatest importance is to equipment designers. Since the modulation index for phase modulation is proportional to the modulating signal and dependent on its frequency, it becomes apparent that the frequency deviation in a phase modulated wave is proportional to both the amplitude and the frequency of the modulating signal. In frequency modulation, however, the frequency deviation is independent of the modulating frequency. This distinction is important to equipment designers because it makes a substantial difference in the design of pre-emphasis networks. The application engineer, on the other hand, must avoid having high-level high frequency signals in any composite modulation applied to the phase modulated transmitter.

When the modulation index of an FM wave is below 0.5, the wave contains exactly the same frequency components as an AM wave, provided both have the same modulating frequency. The basic difference is that the FM sidebands are shifted 90° in phase with respect to the phase relationship of an AM modulated carrier. The manner in which the sideband frequencies are shifted in phase and thus introduce frequency deviation is best shown with the aid of rotating vectors, as in Fig. 5-8.

Detection of FM waves is accomplished by converting frequency variations into amplitude variations employing a circuit called a *discriminator*.

The simplest form of discriminator is a parallel tuned circuit that is resonant to one side of the carrier frequency. The deviations of frequency are on the skirt of the tuned circuit curve, as shown in Fig. 5-9. Although this is an effective means of demodulating FM, it is not very efficient. The most common form of discriminator is the phase shift discriminator, often referred to as the "Foster Seeley," after the circuit designers.

Pulse Modulation

The common forms of pulse modulation are those called (1) *pulse-amplitude modulation* (PAM), in which the amplitude of the pulse changes in accordance with the information to be transmitted; (2) *pulse duration modulation* (PDM), in which the length of the pulse changes to carry the

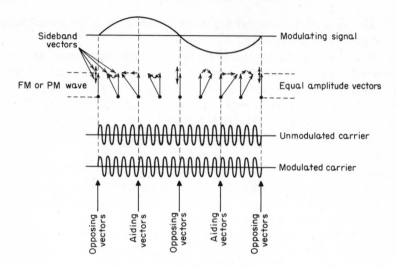

FIG. 5-8. Vector presentation of phase or frequency modulated
wave for small modulation index

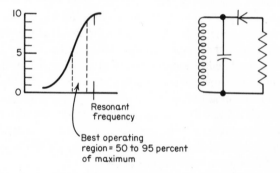

FIG. 5-9. Simple slope detector

information; and (3) *pulse position modulation* (PPM), in which the relative timing of the pulses is changed to transmit the message information.

In pulse modulation, the intelligence contained in the modulating wave is transmitted intermittently rather than continuously, as shown in Fig. 5-10. It is a principle of sampling theory that successive instantaneous measurements of magnitude must equal twice the highest frequency transmitted if they are to provide sufficient information to reconstruct the message.[1] With PAM, PDM, and PPM systems there is usually one pulse for each sample of the information wave. The minimum number of pulses for transmitting multichannel information is computed as follows:

$$P_{min} = 2 \times BW \times N \tag{28}$$

---

[1]Black, H. S., *Modulation Theory*, D. Van Nostrand Co., Chap. 4.

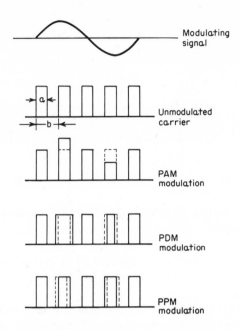

FIG. 5-10. PULSE MODULATION SYSTEMS
PAM modulation is basically not much different from AM modulation, but PDM and PPM modulation depend on accurate positioning of the pulse edges and thus require considerably more transmission bandwidth. (Symbols: a = pulse length, B = repetition rate.)

in which:

P_{min} = minimum number of pulses
BW = highest frequency in the channel
N = number of channels

There are many variations of pulse modulated systems, and just as many combinations of normal modulation with pulse modulated subcarriers. One form of pulse modulation that is becoming increasingly important is called pulse-code modulation (PCM). In this form of modulation, the information signal is broken down into discrete amplitude levels and an amplitude pulse is generated that corresponds to each level. The amplitude pulses are then described by a coded group of pulses that have a uniform amplitude and pulse width. The repetition rate or spacing of the pulses of the code is uniform, and known to the receiver. Therefore, the receiving system simply looks for the presence or absence of a pulse at a known time. In this manner a high degree of coherence is established.

Since the transmitted pulses are all uniform in timing, width, and duration, it is possible to *regenerate* the pulses at each amplifier or repeater. Thus, the accumulated system noise will have no effect on the demodulated signal-to-

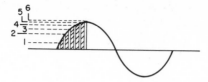

FIG. 5-11.   QUANTIZING OF A CONTINUOUS WAVE
The number of levels used in the quantizer will determine how well the original wave is described by the transmitted signal. The accuracy is directly proportional, and the noise indirectly proportional, to the number of levels.

noise ratio since, as far as the system is concerned, each repeater generates a new noise-free signal.

With proper coding, PCM has been shown to approach the theoretically "best possible" communication system more closely than any other form of modulation in present use. The only noise to appear in the demodulated signal is that resulting from the quantization of the level of the original modulating signal. This noise is indirectly proportional to the number of levels, as shown in Fig. 5-11.

Signals of this type can be transmitted with less fidelity than by any other means because the receiver needs only to make a decision as to the presence or absence of a pulse and can therefore operate with S/N ratios as low as 8 to 10 db.

FM Improvement

A very important characteristic of FM systems lies in the fact that they may be designed and operated in a manner that will greatly reduce the effects of noise and other interference.

Any noise superimposed on an FM signal having a greater amplitude than the noise will cause the envelope of the resulting wave to fluctuate in level and will also produce phase variations. Figure 5-12 is a representation

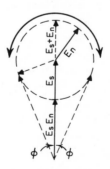

FIG. 5-12.   VECTOR PRESENTATION OF FM SIGNAL AND NOISE

of an FM signal with superimposed noise. The noise can make the signal voltage vary from $E_s - E_n$ when the instantaneous currents are out of phase to $E_s + E_n$ when they are in phase. The phase of the resultant voltage will therefore oscillate between the limit, $\theta = \pm sin\ (E_n/E_s)$, as the noise, E_n, varies in phase relative to the signal voltage, E_s. This will, of course, cause the combined wave to be modulated in phase as well as in amplitude by the noise voltage.

The noise imposed on the FM wave represented by Fig. 5-12 can be prevented from making an appreciable contribution at the receiver output in two ways. First, the receiver should incorporate an effective limiter so that amplitude fluctuations of the received signal will be eliminated. Second, the deviation of the signal at the transmitter should be increased so that, for full modulation, the modulation index is large compared with unity.

When the receiver is made nonresponsive to amplitude fluctuations, the only way noise can appear in the receiver output is through its effect on phase. Therefore, when E_n is less than E_s the modulation index of the noise will always be less than unity. As a result, it is much smaller than the modulation index of the desired signal (which has a large frequency deviation). For example, if a modulating signal of 500 Hz is made to produce a frequency deviation of 50 KHz, then from Eq. 24,

$$\frac{50,000}{500} = 100\ M_s$$

We have a modulation index of 100. In comparison, a noise voltage half as large as the signal $(M_n = 0.5)$ produces a phase deviation only 0.005 times as great as the deviation produced by the signal. From this it can be seen that with a limiter and a large modulation index, a noise impulse that is only slightly below the signal level will be almost completely suppressed. In addition, it becomes obvious that the signal-to-noise ratio of a wideband FM system is superior to that of a narrowband system as long as the signal voltage is greater than the noise.

The relative performance of FM and AM systems on the basis of peak signal and peak fluctuation noise is shown in Fig. 5-13. In an AM receiver the signal-to-noise ratio is the same as the carrier-to-noise ratio (where "carrier-to-noise" refers to the relative amplitudes of the signal and noise prior to demodulation and "signal-to-noise" refers to the signal-to-noise ratio after demodulation) for any ratios greater than zero. This is shown by the 1:1 straight line (designated "AM" system) that rises at a 45-deg angle.

As was seen previously, an FM modulated wave will have a substantially greater signal-to-noise ratio for the higher carrier-to-noise ratios. Figure 5-13 shows how a carrier-to-noise of 20 db is capable of 15 to 16 db less noise for FM signals when the deviation ratio is large. Even small deviation ratios above 0.5 will have noticeably less noise than a straight AM wave.

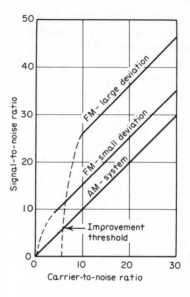

FIG. 5-13. RELATIVE PERFORMANCE OF FM AND AM SYSTEMS

The improvement of signal-to-noise ratio is seen to be constant above a particular point; from this point on, the signal to noise ratio follows the 1:1 straight line angle.

As shown in Fig. 5-13, the point at which the FM curve crosses the AM curve is called the *improvement threshold*. It should be noted that improvement is greater with greater deviation ratios, but the signal level at which any improvement is apparent (sometimes called the *tangential threshold)* is also greater. This increase of required signal is a result of the greater noise power made available from the antenna by the increased bandwidth necessary to handle wideband FM signals. Figure 5-13 shows how the tangential threshold is reduced (assuming optimum BW) as the modulation index is reduced. This reduction continues until the deviation is so low that the FM signal takes on the characteristics of an AM wave.

The amount of improvement obtained from any particular modulation index can be calculated from the formula:

$$R_o = \frac{3}{2} \frac{BW \times f_d^2}{f_m^3} = \frac{3}{2} D^2 \frac{BW}{f_m} \qquad (29)$$

in which:

R_o = improvement ratio
BW = receiver bandwidth
f_d = peak frequency deviation

f_m = highest modulating frequency
D = deviation ratio

It should be kept in mind that R_o is the ratio of improvement due to deviation of the carrier frequency. To obtain the signal-to-noise ratio, this improvement should be added to the carrier-to-noise ratio resulting from signal strength.

Effects of Bandwidth: RF and IF

Insofar as transmission is concerned, it makes little difference if the bandwidth is determined by the RF or IF characteristics of the equipment. As explained previously, the FM signal is not affected by frequency translation, only by multiplication or division.

The bandwidth required by an AM wave is computed as follows:

$$BW = 2M + d \qquad (30)$$

in which:

BW = bandwidth
M = modulation spectrum
d = drift

unless the wave is a single sideband signal, in which case the formula is:

$$BW = M + d \qquad (31)$$

It is this bandwidth that must be passed by the RF and IF circuitry of any AM system. Any portion of the bandwidth suppressed by the filters or tuned circuits will cause the frequency response to be adversely affected.

The proper bandwidth for an FM system, on the other hand, depends not only on the modulation frequency but also on the modulation index. Equation 25 gives a good approximation of the necessary bandwidth for the great majority of the systems. For those few systems that have a requirement for very low distortion, the bandwidth must be wide enough to receive any sidebands containing a significant portion of the transmitted energy.

An examination of the Bessel curve of Fig. 5-6 will give an indication of the power to be expected in the various higher order sidebands. For those cases where the deviation ratio is large and the fidelity must be high, it will be found that the distortion will bear a direct ratio to the sideband energy. For example, if it is desired to have all distortion products 40 db below the signal level, the significant sidebands will be those containing 1.0 per cent of the unmodulated carrier energy. Or if it is desired to increase this signal-to-distortion ratio to 60 db, it will be necessary to accept all sidebands containing 0.1 per cent of the radiated energy.

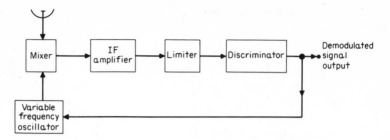

FIG. 5-14. FM FEEDBACK CIRCUIT CONFIGURATION
The demodulated signal output is fed back to the variable frequency
local oscillator to cause its frequency to increase as the frequency of
the incoming signal does, thereby reducing the apparent deviation and
thus the required IF bandwidth.

FM Feedback

The circuit technique referred to as *FM feedback* is a tool used to combat random fluctuation noise. Another name that has become common for this type of circuitry is *frequency compressive feedback;* it is perhaps more descriptive of the phenomenon.

FM feedback is essentially a signal tracking technique. As shown in Fig. 5-14, the frequency of a variable frequency oscillator is made to follow (but never coincide with) the instantaneous frequency of the incoming FM signal in such a way that the difference between the two frequencies still carries the desired message information in linearly compressed frequency variations. This will have the effect of reducing the required receiver bandwidth. Thus, the available noise power will also be reduced by the decrease in bandwidth.

Here we see that the demodulated output is made to change the frequency of the variable frequency oscillator, causing it to track with the incoming signal. This technique is showing great promise in space and satellite communications work. Those who wish to examine it further are referred to the work done with the "Echo" satellites.[1]

FM feedback does have the effect of reducing the modulation index, which must be returned to normal by another means. The use of a very sophisticated demodulator system may be required. The process is quite costly and has not been used as yet in point-to-point microwave systems.

---

[1]Documented in the *Bell System Technical Journal.*

6

Microwave Communications Equipment Loading

Any discussion of communication equipment loading must begin with an understanding of its importance. Present-day point-to-point microwave systems rarely carry only a single channel of information. It is therefore necessary to understand how signals of changing frequency and amplitude combine to produce a complex modulating signal. As the number of signals from the various channels or other sources increase, the complex signal takes on the characteristics of noise with peaking and overload effects that must be controlled. When the circuits of microwave systems are overloaded, intermodulation, crosstalk, and noise will increase in various amounts, depending on the degree of overload. A knowledge of the characteristics of the complex modulating signal is therefore necessary in order to predict their effect on microwave transmission.

Frequency Deviation

Frequency deviation of the FM signal was discussed in the preceding chapter under modulation characteristics, including the effect of the modulation index on the production of sideband energy. It is again necessary to discuss deviation, but this time from the standpoint of a complex modulating voltage. We know that any signal applied to the FM modulator will cause a deviation of frequency. We also know that the deviation must be kept high so that the receiver output signal-to-noise ratio will be satisfactory, and the fluctuation noise will not be exaggerated (see Fig. 5-12). On the other hand, if the modulating signal is too high, the deviation will be greater than the

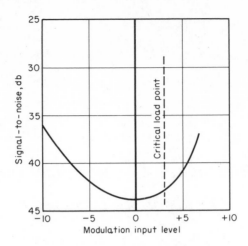

FIG. 6-1. SIGNAL-TO-NOISE RATIO (DB) RELATIVE TO MODULATION
INPUT LEVEL (ARBITRARY UNITS)

receiver bandwidth and noise from distortion due to *intermodulation* will increase.

Figure 6-1 shows how an FM system will have an optimum deviation that will provide the best over-all signal-to-noise performance. The FM deviation for any given load should be adjusted to operate as nearly as possible at this point. If the modulating signal *baseband information* is a single tone or a group of tones with uniform amplitude, the matter of adjustment is a simple one. The level of the tone or tones may be measured or calculated from a knowledge of the signs to be transmitted and adjusted so that continuous operation will always be at the optimum points.

If the baseband information is a group of tones with changing amplitudes, the average combined power of the tones should be calculated from a knowledge of their amplitude and duty cycle, and this level adjusted to the optimum modulation value.

Both of these conditions are fairly simple since the baseband information is either of constant amplitude or has a known small dynamic range. But when the baseband information is the output of a multichannel telephone system — which may or may not have signaling tones present and which may have one or more data or multitone telegraph channels interspersed — the modulating wave tends to take on the characteristics of noise. This complex signal must be adjusted so that it will lie in the proper deviation range for optimum noise performance.

Zero Transmission Level Point

Before proceeding to an analysis of the loading of complex signals, it is important to understand what is meant by the term *zero transmission level point* (abbreviated O-TLP).

In every system composed of different types and pieces of equipment, the operating levels into or from the equipment units must be specified. This level will be the normal input power for the units or device in the over-all system. It is referred to as the *zero level* and will change with the position of the equipment in the circuit. For example, the one normal point of reference in a complex telephone system that is always the same is the toll switchboard. The normal test tone level at this point is zero dbm. If the next piece of equipment that must transmit the telephone signal is the multiplex channel modulator, and it has a normal input level of −16 dbm, a pad must be inserted between them to reduce the level to the −16 dbm power. The new reference level is thus −16 dbm, and any test tone signals measured at this location in the circuit should be at a power level of −16 dbm (equal to 0 dbm at the switchboard).

As the signal progresses through the system from unit to unit, it will experience gains and losses, but each of the units will be designed to handle a particular per-channel test tone level. It is this normal level which is referred to as *zero level,* and the point in the circuit where the measurement is taken must be specified in order to know what the actual power is at that point.

If the level is referred to as a *per-channel level,* the power measured at the input to a device that handles more than one channel will be the summation of the active channels, and this measured value will rise as the number of active channels increase. If the power is referred to as a peak or maximum power, the input is specified as a maximum, and the combined level of the maximum number of active channels should be adjusted to this magnitude. When levels are specified in this manner, the measured power can be expected to decrease as the busy hour passes and more and more of the channels become idle.

Speech Characteristics

In any analysis of the modulating voltage the first question must be, "What is the level of the signal or signals to be used?" Or, if we are considering the baseband information of a multiplex system of "N" channels, "What is the voltage versus time at some point of common reference during the busiest hour of the day?"

Some years ago, B. D. Holbrook and J. T. Dixon of Bell Telephone Laboratories made a study of talker habits in an attempt to obtain information that could be used to determine the load rating theory for multichannel amplifiers.[1] Through the years this information has become the most valuable reference used by engineers the world over when working with the complex signals of multichannel systems carrying speech.

---

[1]Holbrook and Dixon, "Load Rating Theory for Multichannel Amplifiers," Bell Monograph B-1183.

In the determination of speech volumes the standard meters read in "volume units," abbreviated "VU." These units bear a db relationship to each other which tells us that if a reading of −15 VU is obtained for a given talker at a zero level point in the system, the same talker measured at a point in the system where the test level is −10 db will give a reading on a volume indicator that is 10 db below −15 (or at a level of −25 VU, thus maintaining the db relationship). The volume indicator is designed with time constants that will integrate the instantaneous speech power at a syllabic rate. Therefore, the volume of talkers is not a direct measure of power or peak voltage but roughly an average value of the highest readings without considering a rare high peak. However, due to the db relationship, it can be used directly with other measuring instruments as soon as the statistical character of the speech power of a large group of talker information is determined. Then, by use of standard formulas for power addition, this information can be used to estimate the maximum load capacity that a microwave system must handle.

Figure 6-2 is a typical distribution curve of a large group of talkers measured by Holbrook and Dixon at a point of zero reference level. The bell-shaped curve characteristic of a normal Gaussian distribution is evident, with the mean average level being at −12.5 VU and a 1 σ distribution of 5.0 db. These tests were made many years ago with different types of equipment than those presently in use, and tests made more recently here in the United States as well as in Europe indicate that the mean has decreased to a value of −15.0 VU and that the 1 σ distribution now equals 5.3 db.

In subsequent discussions, the occasion will arise to use what is referred to as the "average power talker," that individual whose long term average power multiplied by the number of talkers gives the total long term average power in a multichannel telephone load. It is important to note that the power of the average talker is not the power of the talker whose volume is V_o, but rather the average of the volume distribution. This distribution is normal only in reference to db or the logarithm of the actual power, not the power itself. It therefore becomes necessary to convert the average db distribution to the average power distribution in order to add talker powers correctly.

It has been shown that the volume $V_o − P$ corresponding to the average talker is

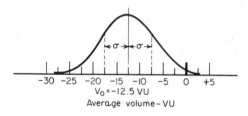

Fig. 6-2. Talker volume distribution

$$V_{op} = V_o + 0.115\,\sigma^2 \tag{32}$$

The power that is equivalent to a zero VU talker is -1.4 dbm. Therefore, if V_o is -12.5 VU and σ is 5.0 db, the average talker power is 12.5 + $(0.115 \times 25) = 9.7$ VU at the zero level point of -1.4 dbm. This corresponds to an absolute of -11.1 dbm at zero level. (Zero VU is equal to -1.4 dbm; that is, a test tone with a magnitude that reads zero on a VU meter will be equal to -1.4 dbm.) This number is reduced to a value of -13.2 dbm when the value of -15 VU is used for V_o.

The above information indicates how difficult it is to attempt to assign a particular amplitude to a talker when trying to determine the load a microwave system must handle. The problem becomes even more complex when considering the fact that talker volume changes with the geographical distance between stations, increasing about 1 db for each 1000 air line miles between stations.

Multichannel Speech

When we try to set up a procedure making use of this information, it is best to express results in values that can be used easily. For load capability it is most convenient to specify a sine wave test tone that the system must carry at the optimum value of transmitter deviation for the talker distribution. If this tone power is selected correctly, then a system that just carries this test tone without undue overloading or noise will be capable of handling the complex load of many telephone talkers satisfactorily. Occasional bursts of noise or distortion caused by overload are not incompatible with toll grade service, provided they do not occur too frequently.

In order to determine the proper sine wave value, two probability distributions must be considered. The first is the number of channels that will be active at any one instant. (A channel is said to be *active* only when it is carrying speech; at any other time it is either *busy* or *idle*.) The chance of a channel being active at any moment during the busy hour is about one in four on large capacity systems. This becomes apparent when you consider that approximately 50 per cent of the time is spent listening. With other pauses in speech and intersyllabic pauses, as well as those in setting up the call, the activity falls to approximately 25 per cent. Thus, the average number of active channels will be about 25 per cent of the total.

In computing the largest values of RMS voltage to be encountered, it is important to remember that the number of channels that may be active at any particular instant in a multichannel system can be anything from zero to N, the maximum number of channels. The percentage of channels that are active increases as the total number of available channels decreases. This is shown in Fig. 6-3 as the curve that is exceeded 1 per cent of the time.

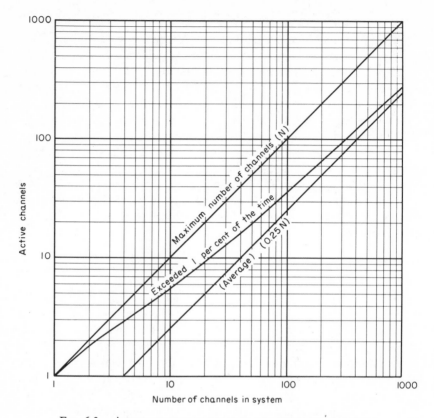

FIG. 6-3. ACTIVE CHANNELS RELATIVE TO AVAILABLE CHANNELS

The other characteristic that must be given consideration in determining the RMS voltages is the probability of having a distribution of mean level talkers. Any very large group would give the distribution shown in Fig. 6-2, but any group expected for smaller systems may be skewed, that is, it may have a larger percentage of loud talkers or a large number of low-level talkers. As with the number of active talkers, this will have a greater effect on a small system than on a large one.

When considering a point-to-point microwave system that must handle a large number of talkers and tones, it is undesirable to consider that all channels have very loud talkers hitting very high peaks at the same time; conversely, it is also unreasonable to expect a small system to have only a few low-level talkers present. The engineering compromise generally adopted is to plan the system so that 99 per cent of the time the system will not be overloaded. For instance, we take the probability distribution of active channels and the probability distribution of talker powers and from these determine the load that will be exceeded only 1 per cent of the time. This value is referred to as the *maximum load* and should be distinguished from the *maximum instantaneous load.*

Before the sine wave test tone that the system must carry can be specified, consideration must be given to how the RMS value of a complex signal, such as discussed here, is obtained and what constitutes a system overload. Therefore, considering a single sideband suppressed carrier system with many channels as the source of modulating voltage, the output signal is the sum of the message sidebands from all the active channels.

As a consequence, the relationship between the instantaneous voltage and the RMS voltage for such a signal has a probability distribution which is difficult to obtain analytically. In systems of more than a few channels experiments have shown that the voltage distribution of the carrier-frequency signal is essentially the same as the voltage distribution of an unmodulated signal that is the sum of the voice frequency signals.

The voice frequency summation was obtained experimentally by combining the recorded speech of many constant-volume talkers. It was found that for a small number of talkers the distribution has high peaks; that is, the voltage peaks (which are much higher than the RMS voltage) occur frequently. But for a number of talkers larger than 64, the instantaneous voltage distribution approaches a more normal curve, as shown in Fig. 6-4.

As extremely large instantaneous voltages do occur, if only rarely, we are forced to define what is meant by *overload.* (This definition will differ from the more familiar one used in conjunction with sine wave signals.) Overload is here defined as the point at which the rated deviation of the system is *just exceeded.* Referring to Fig. 6-1, this would be the point at which the multichannel modulation voltage exceeds the zero level point by 3 db. From this point any increase in voltage will produce noticeable distortion. Any system or amplifier overloaded by a sine wave is usually referred to as being overloaded. The percentage of time that the sine wave exceeds the critical point is usually ignored but should really be specified to allow our statement to be 100 per cent correct.

Here the point of overload is defined as that at which the sine wave peaks just reach a critical value of voltage. Again referring to Fig. 6-1, this

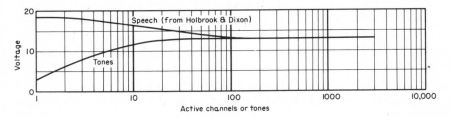

FIG. 6-4. MULTICHANNEL PEAKING FACTOR

would be 3 db above the zero point. This definition is necessary because we are planning to use a sine wave test tone to describe the load of a complex signal.

In our discussion of the complex signal that results from a multitalker speech load, it was shown how the instantaneous voltages occasionally reach very high peaks. It becomes apparent that if the levels are adjusted so that these peaks never exceed the *critical point,* the system will be operating with a very low modulation index nearly 100 per cent of the time. However, very satisfactory transmission is achieved even when the peaks do exceed the critical value, provided they are not sustained peaks or do not occur too frequently. In fact, when considering a large number of talkers, there is no reasonable voltage that will not be exceeded once in a while. For this reason, any consideration of the magnitude of a complex signal must take into account the rare peaks that will occur. Discussions are thus based on the percentage of time the *critical value* will be exceeded. Any sine wave voltage that is determined to equal the critical value is found to be a convenient reference voltage.

Complex Signal Peak Power

To get some degree of order from the facts presented, and to establish some quantitative value of modulating signal, it is convenient to refer to the percentage of time that the peaks will exceed the critical value as ε. The value of ε in any given case is a function of the long term average RMS signal called *maximum load* and the corresponding instantaneous voltage distribution modified by the critical voltage value.

When the critical voltage is frequently exceeded (ε large), the system will have an unnecessary amount of distortion. If the critical voltage is never exceeded (ε small), the system will not be operating at its optimum point.

Tests have determined that quite satisfactory performance can be obtained when the rapidly changing instantaneous voltage exceeds the critical value 0.1 per cent of the time and that distortion becomes objectionable only when this figure is larger.[1] Therefore, returning to the conventional definition of overload, we can say that system overload occurs when the critical value is exceeded more than 0.1 per cent of the time. For example, if the critical value is exceeded only 0.01 per cent of the time, the system is not said to be overloaded since, from our definition, ε is very small.

The voltage of the sine wave that should be carried by a multichannel system in order to handle a complex load satisfactorily must be determined by taking all the foregoing factors into account. That is, one must compute the average power and the load (defined as the power associated with the

---

[1]Holbrook and Dixon, "Load Rating Theory for Multichannel Amplifiers," Bell System Monograph B-1183.

number of active channels) when all the talkers are average and have volumes equal to Eq. 32. We must also add a factor for the probability that the number of channels will be changing and that the talkers will not all be "average." This will place the required value at the 1 per cent power point, or what was previously called "maximum load." At this value we must add an additional allowance for the peak factor of the multichannel signal, as shown in Fig. 6-4. This should be determined by our definition of ε, or the amount of time we will allow the system to overload.

To arrive at a value of sine wave voltage that will equal the multichannel complex load, we must recognize that a sine wave has a peak voltage that is 3 db above the RMS value. It is this peak that the multichannel load will exceed 0.1 per cent of the time. Extensive testing and analysis by the Bell System and the CCIR have determined that the higher efficiency of modern day telephone sets requires a more conservative value of ε; a value of 0.01 per cent is thus recommended for the overload period (this value will be used in the following discussion and calculations).

The peak sine wave voltage corresponding to the multichannel load will be that voltage which is equaled or exceeded 0.01 per cent of the time by the peaks of many telephone talkers.

To avoid the complicated calculations involved with the various probabilities and assumption outlined, R. N. Hunter of the Bell Telephone Laboratories has put the pertinent information in the form of the graph shown in Fig. 6-5. The abscissa is the total number of voice channels in the system and the ordinate is a difference factor, Δc, which is the amount in db by which the critical point must exceed the average busy hour speech load. This factor is commonly referred to as the *multichannel loading factor*. In Fig. 6-5, curves are given for three different values of standard deviation of the talker volumes, based on the following assumptions:

(1) Probability of a channel being active $= 0.25$
(2) Overload period $\varepsilon = 0.01$ per cent
(3) The system must carry the worst 1 per cent combination of talker volumes and number of active channels (1 per cent of the busy hour)

The discussion of system loading that follows is based on the R. N. Hunter graph. Readers who wish to explore the loading philosophy in more detail are referred to Bell System Monograph B 1183.

In order to use Fig. 6-5 effectively, the average busy hour speech load must be determined; this is the combined power of all the active channels during the busy hour.

Equation 32 was used to compute the relative power for one talker, and remembering that a zero VU talker has a power equivalent of -1.4 dbm, the following can be used to determine the average busy hour speech load:

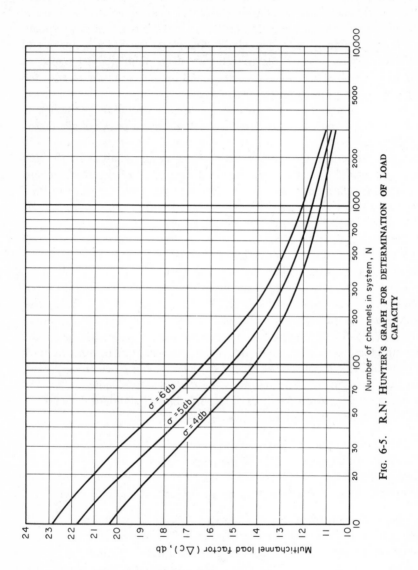

FIG. 6-5. R.N. HUNTER'S GRAPH FOR DETERMINATION OF LOAD CAPACITY

Average power $= (V_o + 0.115 \, \sigma^2 + 10 \, log \, N_a - 1.4)$ dbm   (33)

in which $N_a =$ the number of active channels, or $0.25 \times$ the total channels in the system.

The test tone power is then obtained by evaluating Eq. 33 and adding in the load factor read from Fig. 6-5.

For example, let us suppose we have a mivrowave system that must handle 120 channels. Let us also assume the talker volumes are distributed normally, or as shown in Fig. 6-2. We then have:

$$V_o = -12.5 \text{ VU}$$
$$\sigma = 5 \text{ db}$$

If the system has 120 channels, 25 per cent of the total (see Fig. 6-3) gives us 30 active channels. Evaluating Eq. 33, the average busy hours speech load is

$$- 12.5 + 0.115 \, (5)^2 + \log_{10} 30 - 1.4 = + 3.7 \text{ dbm}$$

For a 120-channel system the value Δc (see Fig. 6-5) should be 14.5 Therefore, the composite signal will equal a level of $+ 3.7 + 14.5$, or $+ 18.2$ db above the zero level. This tells us that the signal will rise 18.2 db above the equivalent level of a single channel test tone at the input to the microwave modulator. Hence, the sine wave power that will just equal the multichannel load should have an RMS value of $+ 15.2$ db at the zero level point, realizing that the peak of this amplitude will be $+ 18.2$ db.

Tone and Speech Combination

When a number of tones of different frequencies are applied to multichannel equipment, the resulting complex signal will also have peaking effects that are important in determining the loading effect of the composite signal. In at least two commonly used types of carrier multiplex equipment, tones are either a large portion, or essentially all, of the load to be handled. Single sideband suppressed carrier (SSB-SC) multiplex equipment, which transmits out-of-band signaling tones, has one -16 db tone for each voice channel. Transmitted carrier equipment, on the other hand, has one -16 db tone for each group of two channels. The carrier levels are of such magnitude that their combined power is the controlling factor.

Another type of carrier equipment in which tones become important is telegraph multiplex equipment. In some cases as many as 20 tones may be present in each voice channel. Since several voice channels in a large system may carry equipment of this type, the resulting load is important.

When two tones of different frequencies and sources are combined in a single circuit, the maximum voltage will be encountered when both tones simultaneously reach their instantaneous peaks. As the number of tones increases, the maximum voltage that may occur also increases and will be the sum of the instantaneous peaks of all tones. Fortunately, the probability of all tones reaching a peak simultaneously becomes very small as the number of tones becomes greater. This is caused by momentary out-of-phase conditions of the tones. It is therefore permissible to consider a peaking factor somewhere between the RMS power of the combined tones and the power corresponding to the in-phase power addition of all of the tones. This compromise value is usually expressed in db. It is a ratio that is practically never exceeded.

When there are 20 or more tones present 100 per cent of the time, a "peak factor" of 13 db added to the RMS power of the combined tones gives a value that is exceeded only 0.003 per cent of the time. (Although this value is much more stringent than $\varepsilon = 0.01$, it has become an accepted value because of the regularity of tone peaking when a number of tones are present continuously.) For fewer than 20 tones, a smaller peak factor may be used, as small as 6 db for two equal level tones. (See Fig. 6-4.) As used in a microwave system, either all tones are of equal level, or a group of tones (such as carrier telegraph) will be of a sufficiently high level, either individually or collectively, that they control the load effect. It is not necessary, therefore, to consider the possibility of all maximum levels occuring simultaneously. A peak power that is based on a peaking factor of 13 db is most realistic.

When these powers are added to determine the combined load, the addition must be performed on a power basis, not on a ratio basis. For example, let us assume that the 120-channel system previously postulated was one that had a −16 db signaling tone present 100 per cent of the time for each channel. Under these conditions the total power of the signaling tones would equate to:

$$(10 \log 120) - 16 = + 4.8 \text{ dbm}$$

This is the RMS power of the 120 signaling tones. These tones have a peaking effect of 13 db (from Fig. 6-4), and therefore, the total peak power will be 13 + 4.8, or + 17.8 db. From our previous calculations for the talker power, we see that the talker load will be + 18.2 db.

Now since these two values are both db ratios, it is necessary to add them as powers. The db ratios are as follows:

$$17.8 \text{ db} = \text{a ratio of } 60$$
$$18.2 \text{ db} = \text{a ratio of } 66$$

Adding these two we have a total of 126, and converting back to db we have 21.0 db. This is the total rise above zero level that will be exceeded 1 per cent of the busy hour from a 120-channel system that has out-of-band tones present at a level of −16 dbm.

Microwave System Loading

In a microwave system the load limiting stage or stages is important to the over-all operation. If the baseband amplifiers are all designed to handle the combined power of the modulation adequately, there will be no sudden breaks in the system noise performance as the overload point is exceeded. There will, instead, be an increase of noise on a gradual basis as the critical point, indicated in Fig. 6-1, is exceeded.

Most microwave systems are designed in this manner, but if the load capability of the system is limited by one of the baseband amplifiers, the overload characteristic is more in keeping with that of feedback amplifiers, and the system will suddenly appear to "break" (a common phenomenon with amplifiers of this type when the overload point is exceeded).

TV Signal Loading

When the signal that is applied to the baseband of a microwave system is a TV picture, the loading effect is similar to a single sine wave. In nearly all cases, the peak-to-peak value of the picture signal is known and can be adjusted for proper deviation.

If the TV signal must carry sound information, too, the sound will be placed on a sub-carrier located above the highest frequency component of the picture signal. The sub-carrier will usually be frequency modulated and will therefore have constant amplitude. The sub-carrier output power is normally on the order of zero to plus 10 dbm and does not have a serious loading effect on the microwave baseband if it is combined with the normal 1 volt peak picture signal.

In order to have optimum loading, the sub-carrier power should be added to the power from the picture channel, and the composite level should be adjusted for the best S/N operation or for the zero point, as indicated in Fig. 6-1.

7

Fundamentals of Antenna Systems

The basic considerations and principles of microwave antennas do not differ substantially from those of any other antenna. As changes in frequency will cause changes in the current and voltage of an ordinary resonant circuit, so too in an antenna will changes of frequency cause variations in the operating parameters. Those characteristics that are most affected are (1) gain, (2) bandwidth, (3) impedance, and (4) radiation pattern. These four factors have practical as well as theoretical interest when it is desired to choose an antenna for a particular application. A lack of knowledge of any of them may result in unsatisfactory system performance.

Whenever the subject of antenna characteristics is considered, the theory of reciprocity should be remembered. This theorem was formulated by Lord Rayleigh and modified to include radio communication by John R. Carson. It states: "If an electromotive force E inserted in one antenna causes a current I to flow at a certain point in a second antenna, then the voltage E applied at this point in the second antenna will produce the same current I (both in magnitude and phase) in a short circuit at the point in the first antenna where the voltage E was originally applied." This theorem fails to be true only when the propagation of the radio wave is appreciably affected by the presence of the earth's magnetic field.

The Rayleigh-Carson theorem shows that in microwave or radio communication between two fixed points, the same conditions are to be expected regardless of which end of the circuit is the transmitting end and which the receiving end. The theorem also provides a means of relating the transmitting and receiving properties of microwave antennas.

70

Fundamental Antenna Parameters

Because of the current and voltage distribution to be found on an antenna at a certain frequency, the inductive and capacitive reactance will balance out, leaving only an effective resistance. The lowest frequency at which this occurs is the *fundamental resonant frequency* of any particular antenna, and it will be found that the length of the antennas is equal to ½ λ. This resonant condition will also occur at higher frequencies that are harmonically related to the fundamental.

Depending on where the power is connected to the radiating element of an antenna, the configuration may be considered as either a series or parallel circuit, as shown in Fig. 7-1. For a resonant dipole antenna fed at the center, the current is a maximum and the voltage a minimum at the point of connection. Consequently, the impedance is low, as shown by the following equation:

$$Z = \frac{V}{I} \text{ ohms} \tag{34}$$

in which:

Z = impedance, in ohms
V = induced emf, in volts
I = induced current, in amperes

The voltage and current distribution along an antenna depends upon its length. This is shown for a fundamental resonant antenna in Fig. 7-2. Here, the current is high at the center and the voltage low, which, in accordance with Eq. 34, will result in a low impedance. Conversely, the voltage is high and the current is low at the ends of a half-wave, which results in a high impedance.

Antenna bandwidth is one of the parameters vital to the operation of antennas that requires careful engineering. Antennas used for microwave point-to-point work frequently require bandwidths of up to 500 MHz; in

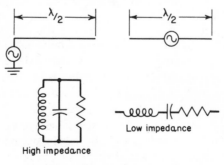

FIG. 7-1. ANTENNA FEED SYSTEMS

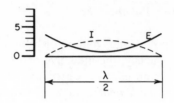

FIG. 7-2. VOLTAGE AND CURRENT DISTRIBUTION ON A HALF-WAVE
DIPOLE ANTENNA

extreme cases, they may require bandwidths of thousands of MHz when operating in one or more bands of frequencies with multiple systems. Generally, most microwave antennas can be broadbanded by changing their physical dimensions or shape in one manner or another. One method often used to broadband an antenna is to transmit energy to the antenna from a transmission line of a higher then normal impedance; the voltage thereby developed at resonance is lower than normal, but the voltage developed at other frequencies is substantially increased. In this manner the response curve of the antenna is flattened, resulting in a better broadband characteristic.

The bandwidth of an antenna is usually specified by the frequency limits, f_1 and f_2, at which the energy reflected from the antenna transmission line mismatch exceeds a particular value. It can be found in terms of a percentage from the equation:

$$\mathrm{BW}\% = \frac{f_2 - f_1}{f_0} \times 100 \qquad (35)$$

in which:

  $\mathrm{BW}\%$ = bandwidth as a percentage of the operating frequency
  f_0 = center of the operating frequency range
  f_1 = lowest operating frequency
  f_2 = highest operating frequency

Antenna Gain

The gain of an antenna is a measure of the antenna's ability to concentrate radiation in a given direction. It is the ratio of the power radiated in a particular direction to the power radiated in the same direction by a standard antenna that determines the effective gain. Since the effective power from a transmitting antenna, or the power available at the output terminals of a receiving antenna, are both dependent upon the antenna's effective area, the effective power gain of an antenna is also dependent on its effective area.

Nearly all antennas are compared to an isotropic radiator, which is a theoretical antenna that has a uniform radiation pattern in all directions. But because on some occasion a half-wave dipole is also used as a standard antenna instead of an isotropic radiator, it is always necessary to specify which was used as reference.

The effective area of an isotropic radiator is given by the formula:

$$A_e = \frac{\lambda^2}{4\pi} \tag{36}$$

in which:

A_e = effective area, expressed in the same units as λ
λ = operating wavelength

In this case, the gain of an isotropic antenna is considered to be unity, and the relation between the effective area and the power gain of any antenna becomes:

$$A_e = \frac{G\lambda^2}{4\pi} \tag{37}$$

in which G = the power gain of the antenna over an isotropic antenna.

If two identical antennas, one transmitting and the other receiving, are placed a distance D apart $(D > 2\,A^2/\lambda$, where A is the maximum aperture dimension) and if the antennas are oriented with their axes coincident, the gain of each antenna may be determined by

$$G = \left(\frac{4\pi D}{\lambda}\right)\sqrt{\frac{P_r}{P_t}} \tag{38}$$

in which:

G = power gain of each antenna over an isotropic antenna
P_r = power received at the antenna terminals, in watts
P_t = power transmitted at the antenna terminals, in watts
λ = wavelengths, in meters

To convert the antenna power gain to decibels, use the following equation:

$$G \text{ (in db)} = 10\,log_{10}G \tag{39}$$

Antenna Directivity

The directivity of an antenna is determined by its lobe pattern and is an important consideration in the selection of an antenna to be used for point-to-point microwave. Figure 7-3 is an illustration of the radiation pattern of an ordinary halfwave dipole.

Here it can be seen that the radiation is a maximum at right angles to the radiating element and a minimum in a direction extending from the ends.

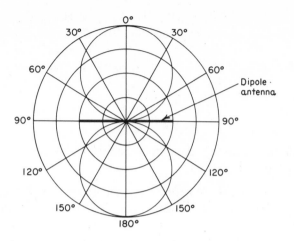

FIG. 7-3. HALF-WAVE DIPOLE RADIATION PATTERN

Figure 7-3 also shows that the dipole will accept signals equally well from any direction at right angles to the antenna and is therefore bi-directional in this plane. For this reason, a dipole used as a radiating element at microwave frequencies will be "backed up" by a reflector that concentrates the antenna's radiation in only one direction.

The ratio of the maximum effective power in the forward direction (the direction in which the antenna is pointing) to the maximum power toward the back is called the *front-to-back ratio*. Expressed in db, it is determined by measuring the voltage or power when the antenna is pointing in the two directions. For example, if an antenna develops 1 volt when it is facing the transmitter and only 0.1 volts when it is revolved 180°, the front-to-back ratio would be 1/0.1, or 10, indicating the antenna is 10 times more sensitive in the forward direction. In the form of an equation, this becomes:

$$\text{Front-to-back ratio (in db)} = 20\, log_{10} \left(\frac{E \text{ volts per meter, front}}{E \text{ volts per meter, back}} \right) \tag{40}$$

$$= 10\, log_{10} \left(\frac{P \text{ watts per meter}^2 \text{ front}}{P \text{ watts per meter}^2 \text{ back}} \right) \tag{41}$$

The lower the power received from the back of the antenna, the less the interaction from signals arriving from this direction. It is not uncommon for a parabolic antenna to have a front-to-back ratio of 40 db, whereas lens and horn antennas frequently have ratios of 50 to 60 db.

In the forward direction the directivity of an antenna will produce an effective increase in transmitting power at the expense of radiation in other directions. This power is called *effective radiated power* (ERP). Thus, ERP is simply an indication of an antenna gain in watts. It may be found by the formula:

$$\text{ERP (in watts)} = G\,P \tag{42}$$

in which:

G = power gain of the transmitting antenna over a reference source
P = power at the terminals of the antenna, in watts

When an antenna is composed of several dipoles or elements in close proximity to each other, the radiation from each element will interfere with the radiation from all of the others. The degree of interference and effect upon the radiation pattern is determined by the relative position of the elements and the magnitude of the currents in the antenna elements.

It does not matter whether the various elements are driven directly by the transmission line or not, so long as the current is of sufficient magnitude. An element that is not physically connected to the transmission lines is called a *parasitic element*. The magnitude and phase relation of its current to the current in the driver element depend upon its tuning. The tuning, which is accomplished by adjusting the length of the element, determines whether it is to act as a reflector sending the energy back toward the driven element or as a director sending its radiated energy in the same direction as the driven element.

To be an effective reflector, a parasitic element must be at least 5 per cent longer than the resonant driver element; conversely, a director must be at least 5 per cent shorter.

When groups of elements are combined in this manner, they cause the impedance of the combination to be reduced below that of a simple dipole — from 30 to 70 per cent, depending on the length and spacing of the reflector elements. The pattern of such a combination is made practically unidirectional at the resonant frequency. In addition, the bandwidth will be decreased to some extent. The gain of the array is increased, however, and may be as great as 4 db for a single reflecting element.

More than one element may be used with a single driver element; the gain will be increased as the number of parasitic elements is increased. The limiting factor of continuing this process for extremely high gains lies in the reduction of the driving impedance. For arrays with many parasitic elements, the driving impedance becomes so low that it is nearly impossible to get any driving power into the array without special coupling and impedance transforming arrangements.

An antenna that contains two or more parasitic elements is often called a "Yagi" antenna or array, and the configuration is usually like that shown in Fig. 7-4. This configuration is often used at the lower microwave fre-

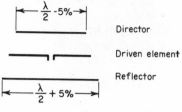

FIG. 7-4. YAGI ANTENNA

quencies and may sometimes have as many as ten parasitic elements. These ten-element arrays usually have very narrow bandwidths and must always have some form of impedance transformer associated with the driver element so that the system will accept power from the transmission lines.

Reflector Antennas

At the higher frequencies in the microwave region, reflectors are often used to modify the radiation pattern of an antenna. Among the various types, the most common are the *flat sheet* reflector, the *corner* reflector, and the *parabolic* reflector. In microwave work, a reflector can be made of any kind of material as long as it has reasonably good electrical conduction; the most common material is aluminum.

Essentially, a reflector intercepts radio energy and reradiates it in another direction in the same manner as a mirror reflects light. Just as some light is scattered by a mirror, some of the radiated power is scattered by the reflection. The amount of power scattered depends upon the relative smoothness of the surface and the type of material used. If the surface variations are no greater than $\lambda/8$, satisfactory reflection results and scattering is low.

The simplest form of reflector is plain flat sheet metal or wire mesh. The gain to be expected from such a configuration is limited to about 9.2 db over an isotropic antenna when the spacing between the driver element and the reflecting surface is equal to 0.1 λ. A flat reflector does not appreciably change the radiation pattern but simply converts the normal bi-directional pattern of a dipole to a larger unidirectional pattern by reflecting the backward radiation.

Bending the plain sheet reflector into a corner reflector will give gains higher than the sheet reflector by compressing the wave into a beam. Still higher gains become possible by extreme concentration or beaming of the radiated energy using parabolic reflectors, which can be made in very large sizes with very narrow beam angles.

Antenna Feed System

We have seen that at microwave frequencies the antenna system is usually composed of one or more reflectors and a means to properly inject or focus the RF energy into the system. The device used to excite the antenna may take several different forms but must be designed to direct as much energy as possible into the reflector (most frequently a parabola). The efficiency of an antenna system depends upon how true to a perfect parabola the reflector is and how well the energy is directed onto the reflecting surface. The antenna feed is located at the focal point of the reflecting parabola, and is usually designed to provide as good an impedance match to space as possible.

At the lower microwave frequencies, the most common injection system is composed of a group of two or more simple halfwave dipoles. One of these will be excited by the transmitter; the others are parasitically excited and phased so that they will direct the RF energy into the reflecting parabola. The excited dipole often is only 2 to 3 inches in length. This system is quite frequency sensitive and should be selected to resonate in the middle of the desired operating bandwidth. At the lowest microwave frequencies (450 to 1000 MHz) the whole antenna takes on a modified Yagi configuration with the exciter pointing in the direction of transmission and the parabola acting as a reflector.

At microwave frequencies above 2000 MHz the injector most commonly used is a horn configuration. It may be waveguide or coaxial fed, but the antenna injector is the whole horn. A horn feed is a very good and simple means of obtaining an impedance match between the transmission line and space. The degree of match is improved as the horn becomes larger and longer. The horn injection system has the added advantage of being less frequency sensitive, the bandwidth often equaling several thousand MHz.

There are many other smaller and shorter injection schemes used to excite antenna systems. In nearly all cases, however, these are resonant launchers and cannot be used at more than one frequency; moreover, they are undesirable for multisystem installations that require a bandwidth of more than a few per cent. In addition, some of them do not adequately illuminate the reflector; consequently, the expected antenna gain is often not realized.

Parabolic Antenna

Parabolic antennas are available in sizes from 1 ft in diameter to over 120 ft in diameter. When used at microwave frequencies above 2000 MHz, however, they rarely are larger than 10 ft. The gain available is greater as the antenna size is increased because of the narrower beam and increased directivity. A typical parabolic antenna is shown in Fig. 7-5. Figure 7-6 is a nomogram showing how the gain of a parabolic reflector antenna varies with size and frequency.

For a particular diameter, the characteristics of the reflected wave are

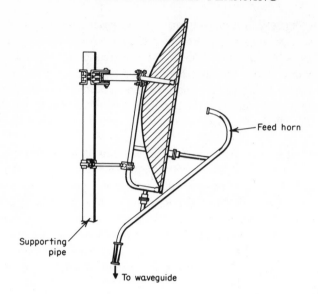

FIG. 7-5.   PARABOLIC ANTENNA (COURTESY, MARK PRODUCTS)

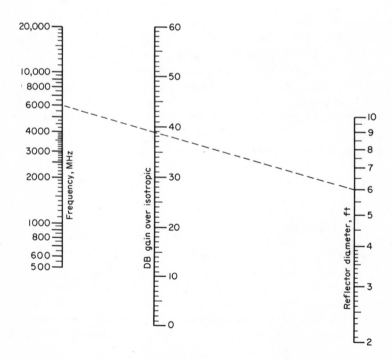

FIG. 7-6.   PARABOLIC ANTENNA GAIN BASED ON 55 PER CENT
EFFICIENCY

best when a shallow dish is used. Thus, a parabola with a long focal length
is called for. However, the incident illumination thereby provided is not as
good as that with a shorter focal length, and the result is a somewhat reduced
efficiency. Focal length is extremely important and should be selected with
care. If it is an even number of quarter wavelengths, the direct and reflected
radiation in an axial direction from the exciter will tend to cancel the center
region of the beam. On the other hand, if it is held within the limits given
by the formula:

$$\text{Focal length} = \frac{N\lambda}{4} \tag{43}$$

in which N is an odd number of wavelengths, the direct and reflected radiation will reinforce the center region of the beam.

When it is not possible to prescribe the focal length of a parabola because of mechanical configuration or for some other reason such as operation
with two or more nonharmonically related frequencies, direct radiation from
the driver element can be reduced substantially and the reflector illumination
improved by the use of a parasitic or flat sheet element close to the dipole.
This secondary reflector is located in such a way as to concentrate most of the
radiation from the dipole into the parabolic dish.

The major factor contributing to the gain or beaming action of a parabolic reflector is the total area of the reflecting surface. For a uniformly
illuminated dish, the reflected beam angle is proportional to the wavelength
and indirectly proportional to the diameter. The beam width between half
power points for a large circular reflector may be found from the formula:

$$\text{Beam width (in degrees)} = \frac{58}{D\lambda} \tag{44}$$

in which $D\lambda$ is the diameter of the reflector aperture, in terms of wavelength.
The beam width given by this formula is actually an "equivalent angle" —
the cross section of the cone where the radiated energy is expected to
concentrate.

The beam of a parabolic antenna starts out in a cylindrical form and
then diverges progressively after a certain point into a conical beam, as
shown in Fig. 7-7. The cylindrical portion is called the *beam-forming* or
Fresnel region, and the conical portion is called the *Fraunhofer region.* Since
the cylindrical region has a substantially uniform field and a parallel beam,
any material with a high reflection coefficient and sufficient cross section
located there will reflect the radiated energy with very little loss. For this
reason it is advisable to keep the beam-forming region free of any undesired
obstructions when locating antennas on rooftops or in the vicinity of trees or
power distribution installations.

The beam-forming, or Fresnel, region has a maximum distance that is

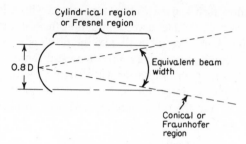

FIG. 7-7.   PARABOLIC BEAM FORMING REGION

proportional to the square of the aperture diameter and inversely proportional to the wavelength. It is given by the formula:

$$\text{Fresnel region maximum distance} = \frac{D \lambda^2}{2 \lambda} \qquad (45)$$

in which, as before, $D \lambda$ is the diameter of the reflector aperture, in terms of wavelength.

The Fresnel region is often used advantageously by antenna systems using passive reflectors. If the distance between the antenna and the passive reflector is not greater than the cylindrical Fresnel region, the passive reflector will reflect the energy with very little loss. The gain of a parabolic reflector can be calculated in decibels from the formula:

$$\text{Gain} = 10 log_{10} 6D\lambda^2 \qquad (46)$$

This equation assumes perfectly uniform illumination of the reflector. In actual practice it is very difficult to obtain uniform illumination; with dipole exciters, it is impossible. Therefore, a more accurate answer from the above formula will be obtained by using an equivalent reflector diameter of 70 to 80 per cent of the actual diameter. Figure 7-6 can be used to determine the gain of typical antennas at frequencies from 500 to 20,000 MHz.

Parabolic reflectors are most commonly made of solid aluminum but in some cases they are made of wire mesh to reduce wind loading. Whether the reflector is made of solid or mesh material makes little difference unless the frequency of transmission is very high. The mesh material does not become a good reflector at very high microwave frequencies because too much energy is passed directly through the mesh. The maximum size of the openings in the mesh has a wavelength relationship that usually limits the use of this material to the lower microwave frequencies. Ordinarily this limitation does not introduce a hardship because the wind loading of a particular antenna system is proportional to its size, and the larger antennas most affected by wind are not normally used at the higher microwave frequencies. If the openings in the mesh are square, the *edge lengths* of the holes should be less than $\lambda/8$. If the mesh is composed of a sheet with round holes, the *diameter* of the holes should be less than $\lambda/8$. For example, a copper screen woven of No. 17 B & S wire with openings ⅛-in. square will reflect about 95.5 per cent of the incident power at a wavelength of 9 cm.

Antenna Reflector Combinations

As discussed briefly in the previous paragraphs, any reflecting surface placed in the Fresnel region of a parabolic antenna will reflect the microwave energy with very little attenuation. Under ideal conditions of spacing and illumination the antenna reflector combination can actually show a gain of 1 or 2 db over the parabolic antenna used alone.

This effect is advantageously used in many installations by placing the antenna at ground level and reflecting the signal from a surface located at the top of the antenna tower, as shown in Fig. 7-8. Even if the possible added gain of this combination is not realized, the reduced loss of shorter waveguide runs is a very real advantage.

There are many possible antenna reflector combinations; the one used will be dictated, to a large extent, by the particular installation. In general, however, the reflector must be of sufficient size to intercept practically all of the energy transmitted by the antenna.

Mechanically speaking, the antenna is usually mounted about 10 ft above ground facing upward. The reflector is located at the top of the tower, inclined at a 45-deg angle, and faced in the direction of desired transmission. Once they are installed, nothing should be allowed to come between the antenna and the reflector. Guy wires and any lighting fixtures must be attached to the tower in such a manner as will keep this area completely unobstructed.

When a reflector is mounted on a tower it effectively becomes the radiating surface. It should be located at the height above ground that provides adequate line-of-sight clearance.

Most passive reflectors are just large, flat, metallic surfaces; energy is re-transmitted from their illuminated area. Some reflectors, however, can be shaped into a curved surface. This is usually done by pulling up on a series of rings attached to the back surface of the reflector, resulting in a slight gain improvement. The added gain occurs because the curvature tends to resemble a very large parabola that has a focal point at the position of the illuminating antenna. Performance curves for various standard reflectors show that when they are properly adjusted, gains of up to 3 db may frequently be realized.

When curved reflectors are installed, they should always be adjusted. Otherwise, since they are usually more flexible than a standard flat reflector, the reflecting surface might become slightly convex and cause beam scattering. In some cases, the weight of the adjusting rings alone is enough to cause

FIG. 7-8   PLACEMENT OF PASSIVE REFLECTORS AT THE TOP OF A TOWER
TO REFLECT SIGNALS TO AND FROM PARABOLIC ANTENNAS AT THE BASE

the reflecting surface to become convex if they are not adjusted or supported.

One word of caution when considering antenna reflector combinations: In practically every case there are strong minor lobes of radiation created by the reflector. When the antenna system is aligned along the propagation path, great care should be exercised to avoid leaving the system on a minor lobe. These minor lobes can shift severely under varying weather conditions and result in deep fades. An additional word of caution: The parabolic antenna points upward with its opening facing the sky and, unless provided with a weatherproof cover, rain, leaves, and other foreign objects may fall into the dish and absorb microwave power.

Reflectors Beyond the Fresnel Region

When the reflector is located beyond the Fresnel region of an antenna, it is usually quite large and thus rarely mounted on a tower. Its most common use in these circumstances is to reflect or bounce the signal around or over an obstruction. For this purpose, the total path length is normally about ½ to ⅔ the length of a normal hop. Installation of more than one reflector in a particular path is very rare because space loss accumulates too rapidly. This accumulation comes about because the space loss is inserted twice rather than only once, as shown in Fig. 7-9. This illustration reveals that the space loss via the reflector is much greater than the direct path loss. Although the actual path loss would not be as great as that indicated (because of some gain introduced by the reflector), it would still be considerably greater than that on a one-hop direct path.

Reflectors are sometimes made of gratings or screens to reduce the wind loading. The reflector may be ridged or reinforced woven metal screen, or it may be reinforced perforated sheet metal. The openings in either type of material are limited in size by the frequency of operation. If the openings are square, as in woven screen, the edge length of the holes should be less than one-eighth the wavelength. If the metal is punched with round holes, the diameter of the holes should be less than one-eighth the wavelength.

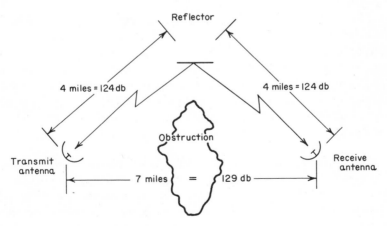

Fig. 7-9. Accumulated reflector loss

A reflector must be located and oriented very carefully; usually the assistance or advice of someone who has done the job before is required. Initial accuracy is essential since very little adjustment is possible once the reflector is in place.

The limited adjustment available makes it necessary to set the reflectors on firm foundations located below the frost line in order to prevent the normal heaving of the ground during freezing and thawing seasons from affecting the orientation.

Passive Repeaters

A passive repeater is very similar to a flat reflector except that it is much more flexible and more open to the correction of errors in orientation. The angle of incidence and the angle of exit need not be the same for this system.

Mechanically, the passive repeater takes the form of two parabolic antennas connected back to back. One of them faces in the direction of the transmitter, the other in the direction of the receiver. This arrangement permits gains and losses to be more readily calculated from antenna and waveguide charts. Space loss is inserted twice with a passive repeater, just as it is with a flat reflector. It can also be more costly from an equipment standpoint than the flat reflector.

Other Types of Antenna

Several other types of antenna can be used for microwave transmission, most of them very special and designed for specific applications. The parabolic antenna is by far the most common and versatile, but most of the others operate just as well.

(1) *Corner reflector*   The corner reflector is a modification of a cylindrical parabolic reflector. In practical form, a corner reflector consists of two flat sheets of reflecting material at right angles to each other. Angles greater or less than 90 deg can also be used, although at angles below about 60 deg no net advantage is realized. When a dipole radiator is located within the plane bisecting the corner angle and parallel to the corner angle, gains of 10 to 15 db over an isotropic antenna can be realized. Figure 7-10 gives some design and gain information.

(2) *Lens antenna*   A lens antenna is a device that is transparent to microwave radiation and has a dielectric constant different from dry air. Its operation is based on the Fresnel principle of focusing light. The delay device is made of lucite or polystyrene. Sometimes it is foamed to reduce weight.

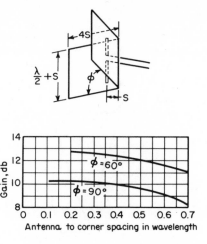

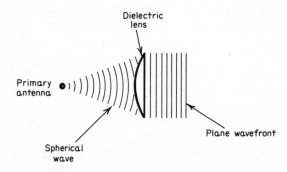

Fig. 7-10. Corner reflector antenna

The delay lens material acts to increase the electrical path of a spherical wave front, introducing a retarding effect. Since the retarding material is usually thickest in the center, it causes greater delay at the center than at the edges. The effect is to convert the spherical wavefront to a plane wavefront, as shown in Fig. 7-11.

All lens type antennas change a spherical wavefront to a plane wavefront or, in reverse, a plane wave to a spherical. In the transmitting direction, the spherical wavefront is converted to a plane wavefront, thus reducing its divergence as it proceeds along the propagation path. In the receiving direction, the delay lens converts a plane wavefront back to a spherical wavefront, thus converging or concentrating the energy at the primary antenna. This is true even when a lens antenna is used to receive a spherical wavefront radi-

Fig. 7-11. Lens antenna delay characteristic
The wave radiated from the primary antenna in a spherical wavefront is sufficiently delayed by the lens to cause the curvature of the wavefront to become a plane.

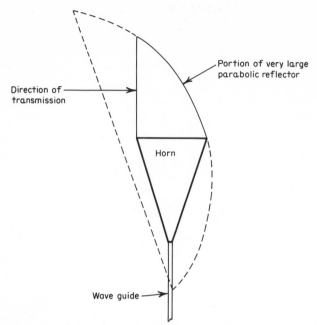

Portion of very large
parabolic reflector

Direction of
transmission

Horn

Wave guide

FIG. 7-12. HORN REFLECTOR ANTENNA

ated from a non-lens type antenna because at the distances involved, the spherical wave is so large and the amount of curvature is so small that it can be considered a plane wavefront.

The lens antenna usually has a much wider bandwidth than a parabola as it contains nothing that is frequency sensitive. In most cases the primary antenna is a horn because a horn can give greater efficiency as a result of more compatible mechanics and better impedance match.

Lens antennas in common use above 3000 MHz usually have apertures that are nearly 10 feet on a side, resulting in gains up to 40 db, depending on the operating frequency.

(3) *Horn reflector*   The horn reflector antenna is a modification of a standard parabolic reflector antenna system, as illustrated in Fig. 7-12. This configuration is in reality a portion of a very large parabola that is illuminated nearly 100 per cent by a horn type antenna. The reflector and antenna are assembled in such a manner that microwave energy is transmitted at right angles to the waveguide and horn.

In this configuration very high gains and efficiencies can be realized, thanks to the large horn as well as the very large parabola. Since it has a very wide bandwidth, like the delay lens, it is often used on more than one band of microwave frequencies at the same time. At the upper microwave frequencies, gains in excess of 40 db are not uncommon.

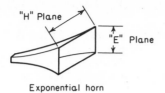

Exponential horn

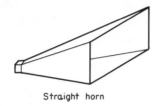

Straight horn

FIG. 7-13. HORN ANTENNA

(4) *Horn antenna*   The horn antenna is basically just a flared section of waveguide, as shown in Fig. 7-13. The transition from waveguide to air is sometimes given an exponential taper, especially at very high frequencies, in order to minimize reflections of the guided wave. However, horns with straight flares are more common because they are easier to manufacture. Besides, whether the antenna has an exponential flare or a straight flare makes little difference except at extremely high frequencies where the wavelength is in the order of millimeters and the horn is only 3 to 5 in. in length.

The radiation pattern of a horn is basically a function of the field distribution within the aperture. For a particular horn aperture, directivity is greatest when the field distribution is uniform. Variations of field intensity across the aperture will have the effect of skewing the pattern and reducing the directivity. Very uniform field distribution can be obtained by the use of long horns with small flare angles.

Long horn antennas with exponential tapers are commonly used as standard antennas because their patterns and gains are easily predicted and are not normally adversely affected by frequency changes. These antennas can be designed to give an almost perfect match between the transmission line and free space, resulting in very low antenna reflection and maximum propagated energy.

Since the beam width and gain characteristics for circular horns are the same as for a parabolic reflector, the same formulas can be used. For rectangular horns of optimum length, the beam width at half power points is approximately as follows:

$$BW = \frac{60}{E\,\lambda} \tag{47}$$

in which $E\,\lambda$ is the E plane aperature in free space wavelength.

The gain of a rectangular horn, which is uniformly illuminated, can be calculated from the following equation:

$$\text{Gain (in db)} = 10\log_{10} 4.5\ E\ \lambda\ H\lambda \tag{48}$$

in which $E\ \lambda$ is the E plane aperture in free space wavelength and $H\lambda$ is the H plane aperture in free space wavelength. From these equations it is easy to see how the gain of a horn antenna increases as length and aperture is increased.

8

Microwave Equipment

Power Generation

Conventional oscillators using lumped capacitance and inductance circuits will operate reasonably well, although with somewhat poor efficiency, at frequencies as high as 250 MHz. Above this frequency special circuits and techniques must be used in order to obtain sufficient microwave energy to make the effort feasible. At frequencies of 250 MHz and above, the spacing of the elements of conventional vacuum tubes becomes an appreciable fraction of an operating wavelength. At these high frequencies even straight pieces of wire are found to have sufficient inductance and capacitance to affect the circuit operation adversely.

First attempts to solve the problem of electron transit time (the finite time for an electron to travel from cathode to plate) were directed toward reducing the spacing of the elements within the tube as well as the length of the connecting leads. This process is satisfactory up to nearly 500 MHz for low power tubes but leads to severe oscillation, noise, and arcing between elements for the larger transmitting-type tubes.

At frequencies above 500 MHz the tubes are designed around a different configuration known as a planar-type triode. The familiar 2C39 lighthouse tube is a typical example of the planar triode. Figure 8-1 shows the construction of a ceramic type planar triode. The advantage of this form of construction lies in the fact that the various tube elements can be coupled directly to the circuit elements, reducing lead inductance and stray capacitance.

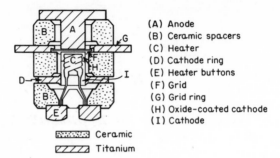

(A) Anode
(B) Ceramic spacers
(C) Heater
(D) Cathode ring
(E) Heater buttons
(F) Grid
(G) Grid ring
(H) Oxide-coated cathode
(I) Cathode

▓▓▓▓▓ Ceramic
▨▨▨▨ Titanium

FIG. 8-1. CROSS SECTION OF GE 7077 CERAMIC PLANAR TRIODE

As the frequencies continue to go higher (above 1000 MHz) even the planar tubes become inefficient, and it is necessary to generate microwave power in another manner because the interelectrode transit time of the electrons becomes too long. It was because of the need for a generator of power at frequencies above 1000 MHz that Russell and Sigurd Varian developed the Klystron.

Klystron tubes

Power generation above 1000 MHz was almost universally accomplished (until the recent trend toward the use of multistage solid state devices) with *klystron* oscillators. These fall into two main categories: the *reflex* klystron and the *multi-cavity* klystron.

The reflex klystron is a rather low-efficiency tube (approximately 3 per cent) but still a very convenient device for low-power transmitters and receiver local oscillators. The maximum power capability of these tubes is rarely greater than 1 watt. The multi-cavity klystron is much more efficient (20 to 40 per cent) and can be designed to generate substantially higher power levels.

In operation, the two-cavity klystron has an electron gun that gives off a stream of electrons; these electrons are focused into a beam and directed into an evacuated drift space, as shown in Fig. 8-2. The beam is passed

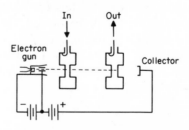

FIG. 8-2. BASIC TWO-CAVITY KLYSTRON

through an *input cavity,* which is resonant at the operating frequency. The input cavity contains an electric field that changes at the operating frequency and accelerates or retards the speed of the beamed electrons. Those that are accelerated are propagated through the drift space at a higher than normal velocity. Those that are retarded proceed through the drift space at a lower than normal velocity. As they proceed through the drift space, the retarded electrons are overtaken by those traveling at normal speed, and those at normal speed, in turn, are overtaken by accelerated electrons. At a particular spacing from the input cavity, therefore, the electrons bunch together, producing cyclic power. The beam is then passed through a second cavity called the *output cavity.* This cavity is used to collect the energy contained in the bunched electron beam and couple it to the output circuit.

The action described above results in an amplified output. If some of the output energy is fed back to the input cavity in the proper phase and at the required amplitude, the tube can be made to oscillate and thus become a microwave power generator.

Reflex Klystron

The reflex klystron is a modified version of the two-cavity klystron oscillator. This tube contains only a single resonant cavity, which acts as both buncher and collector. In the reflex klystron the electrons from the gun pass through the grids twice under the influence of the *repeller,* which carries a high negative potential (see Fig. 8-3). As in the two-cavity klystron, the electrons focused into a beam are *velocity modulated* (changed in speed) in their first passage through the cavity grids. They proceed into the drift space toward the repeller, where they are turned back by its high negative charge to pass again through the cavity in the opposite direction; they are finally collected at the accelerating anode of the electon gun. In the drifting period between their two passages through the cavity, the electrons tend to become bunched in accordance with the resonant frequency of the cavity.

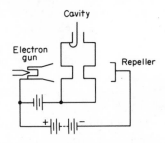

FIG. 8-3.   REFLEX KLYSTRON

When the repeller voltage is properly adjusted, the returning electron bunches will pass through the cavity in such phase as to give up energy to the cavity.

In addition to its smaller and simpler structure, the reflex klystron has the added advantage of being simple to modulate. The output frequency can be varied within limits, above and below the natural resonant frequency of the cavity, by varying the negative voltage applied to the repeller. This is the characteristic that is used most effectively in many microwave transmitting systems.

Solid state power generation

In recent years a new means of generating microwave power has resulted from the extensive development effort directed toward solid state circuit elements. This method makes use of a device known as a *varactor,* a type of semiconductor diode, to develop fairly large amounts of harmonic energy. These techniques have been effective at frequencies up to 8 GHz.

By definition, in its broadest form, a varactor is a reactance that changes in magnitude and may be either inductive or capacitive. In general usage, however, the term varactor has come to mean a junction diode designed specifically to make use of the nonlinear capacity-vs.-voltage characteristic of a PN junction in the reverse bias region or in the forward region close to its origin.

These units have come to be important to VHF and microwave systems as a result of the high efficiencies obtainable in doubling, tripling, or quadrupling circuits. Efficiencies in the order of 50 to 90 per cent are common for single-stage devices. Over-all efficiencies of multistage circuits are lower, of course; but when considered on the basis of primary power to RF, the efficiency compares favorably with that of reflex klystrons and many other devices. The high efficiency of these devices is obtained because varactor diode nonlinearity is reactive rather than resistive, as is common with other types of multipliers. The residual power loss that does occur in these units is associated with the minor parasitic series resistance of the diodes and the circuit resistance of associated networks.

A pictorial representation of the principle used is shown in Fig. 8-4. The rather severe distortion of the applied wave necessary to implement harmonic generation is easily seen. The sine wave at the bottom of the figure represents the input charge variation as a function of time. To the right is shown the voltage wave, which results from the charge-vs.-voltage curve. This figure is a considerably simplified representation of actual conditions. In reality, the charge, voltage, and current waves are all severely distorted and much more complex than those shown.

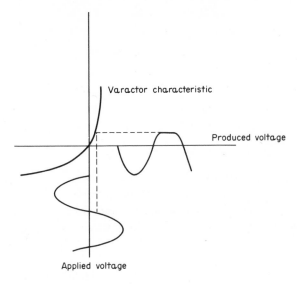

Varactor characteristic

Produced voltage

Applied voltage

FIG. 8-4. HARMONIC GENERATION

Varactor basic circuits

The basic circuit configuration of a varactor multiplier is merely a combination of two resonant circuits coupled together through a common load impedance, which is the varactor diode. Since the varactor impedance is usually quite small compared to the reactance presented to undesirable frequencies in either of the two separate loops, there is a natural division of current (see Fig. 8-5). A large portion of the fundamental current flows in the input circuit, and practically all of the second harmonic current flows in the output circuit.

The basic configuration of tripler and quadrupler circuits is the same. A basic tripler circuit is shown in Fig. 8-6, and a complete schematic is shown in Fig. 8-7. Through resonant frequencies are coupled together by the common varactor impedance to form the basic tripler configuration. One

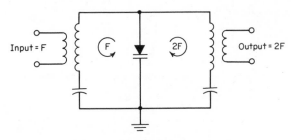

Input = F   F   2F   Output = 2F

FIG. 8-5. VARACTOR DOUBLER

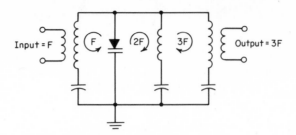

FIG. 8-6. VARACTOR TRIPLER

loop resonant with the varactor diode at the fundamental is coupled to the input. Another loop resonant at the second harmonic is added in shunt with the varactor. This is referred to as an *idler* and has been found to be necessary to obtain maximum efficiency by allowing the second harmonic currents to flow in the network. The third loop is resonant with the diode at the third harmonic and is also coupled to the output.

When used as a quadrupler, the basic configuration remains the same except that the output loop is resonant to the fourth harmonic instead of the third. The idler remains tuned to the second harmonic.

A practical circuit usually requires a few more components and more design than are shown in these basic circuits since basic circuits are merely simple tuned networks and frequently have quite narrow response. If the harmonic multiplier is to be used effectively in a transmitter, it must be capable of passing a band of frequencies so that any modulation information present will not be unduly distorted. A practical tripler circuit capable of being driven with 20 watts at 150 MHz and of delivering 10 watts at 450 MHz is shown in Fig. 8-7. This generator should be tuned very carefully in order to avoid tuning to a higher order harmonic.

Circuits L_1/C_1 and L_2/C_2 should be tuned to the drive frequency of 150 MHz. L_3/C_4 should be tuned to 300 MHz, whereas L_4/C_5 and L_5/C_7

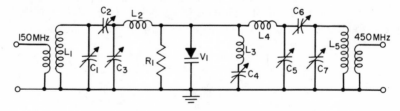

FIG. 8-7. VARACTOR MULTIPLIER CIRCUIT
C_1, C_3, C_4, C_5, and $C_7 = 1 — 9$ μμf
C_2 and $C_6 = 0.4 — 2.0$ μμf
L_1 and $L_2 = 7$ turns, ¼-in. diam., No. 20
$L_3 = 5$ turns, ¼-in. diam., No. 20
L_4 and $L_5 = 3½$ turns, ¼-in. diam., No. 20
$R_1 = 33$ K (carbon)
$V_1 = MA$ 4061B

should be tuned to 450 MHz. As a final test, the frequency of output as well as the output power should be carefully measured in order to assure proper tuning. A swept frequency should then be transmitted through the harmonic generator in order to optimize the bandwidth.

Varactor bias

Some frequency multiplier circuits can be very successfully driven into the forward region and thus provide a greater capacity variation resulting in improved efficiency. When a varactor is driven into the forward region, positive carriers in the semiconductor material are actually driven across the junction and can be removed on the next operating cycle, provided the *combination lifetime* of the semiconductor material prevents recombination.

This effect has been called *injection capacitance* and occurs abruptly between 0 and approximately + 0.5 volts. Not all varactor diodes will display this phenomenon strongly, but the bias voltage should be selected so as to take advantage of it whenever possible.

A form of self bias is usually recommended as the most practical. This is the form of bias used in the circuit shown in Fig. 8-7. It is accomplished by shunting the varactor diode with a suitable carbon resistor to provide the path across which the bias voltage is developed.

The self-bias method will accommodate wide variations in driver power and compensate for the small changes in characteristics as varactor diodes are changed or replaced. A bias resistor should be chosen to allow the varactor to be fully driven and, when possible, to take advantage of the heavy charge storage potential of the forward region between 0 and + 0.5 volts.

Varactor Power Capability

Because all of the power supplied in the output of a varactor-type harmonic multiplier must be supplied by the RF driver, care is required in selecting the varactor types used in early stages of a multiplier chain. The maximum power output capability of a particular harmonic chain may sometimes be limited by the input stages or the driving source, if (as is frequently the case) it is also a semiconductor device.

The power handling capability of most configurations is limited by the varactor breakdown voltage, and therefore the input power must be limited to prevent its exceeding this value. Most multiplier configurations involve an impedance of from 10 to 100 ohms, with the majority favoring the lowest value. This lower impedance, of course, will tend to limit the peak voltages encountered in commonly used configurations.

Increasing the voltage capability of a diode usually means increasing its series resistance (R_s) and, for this reason, the RF losses. It is therefore desirable to choose the lowest voltage diode compatible with the anticipated operation. Large junction areas accompany lower values of R_s and better thermal dissipation, so that average power capability is approximately proportional to junction area. Charge storage or injection capacitance will also enhance the power handling capability of a varactor.

Varactor Modulation

Modulation of varactor harmonic multipliers falls into the same category of complexity as that of any other form of harmonic device. Within the normal passband of the multiplier, modulation that does not depend on instantaneous or sudden changes of amplitude can be readily accomplished. Frequency or phase modulation is very satisfactory, providing the multiplied deviation that accompanies the frequency multiplication is acceptable. In fact, if the system is designed properly, the modulation can become extremely linear. For example, a 50 MHz drive signal that is deviated 0.5 MHz when multiplied to 6 GHz will have experienced a multiplication of 120 times. The 0.5 MHz deviation will also be multiplied by a factor of 120 and will be increased to 60 MHz. This is an increase of the modulation index, which should be carefully considered in the design of any FM system. When harmonic multipliers are used in this manner, the bandwidth of each stage must be sufficient to pass the sidebands of significance, or undesirable distortion will result. Simultaneous amplitude and frequency modulation will also result, but amplitude variations will be suppressed more in a varactor multiplier than in any other type.

Phase modulation, as shown previously, is a form of FM and therefore can be expected to give similar results. When the phase of the input is shifted, the phase of the output will also shift, and the output shift will be greater by a factor equal to the total multiplication ratio.

In common FM, or phase, modulators, modulation linearity usually varies indirectly with the amount of deviation so that good linearity can easily be obtained for small values of deviation. Taking advantage of the deviation multiplication that occurs in a frequency multiplier is an excellent means of obtaining good linearity with wide swings of the transmitted carrier.

Phase-reversal modulation is a form of modulation usually associated with binary digital transmission. This system of modulation involves a reversal of signal phase in order to transmit the information, and as such, is similar to FM. Therefore, this system can transmit the information (binary) through a harmonic multiplier with lower distortion than is possible with AM forms of modulation.

All forms of harmonic generation devices depend upon nonlinearity as a mode of operation, and the varactor networks are no exception. As can be seen from the curve in Fig. 8-4, varactors depend on a saturation condition for their high efficiency as harmonic generators. Therefore, faithful reproduction of complex AM waveforms should not be expected. In some cases, some forms of deeply modulated AM signals can be passed through a varactor network with an acceptable degree of linearity, but as a rule any AM modulation should be accomplished following the output of the harmonic generator. Since strong AM distortion effects are most prevalent in multipliers that use multiple stages, no attempt should be made to make them pass AM information.

Pulse modulation is a form of AM, and when the pulse rates are low enough to allow the transients to decay (as a result of the ringing effects of tuned circuits), operation will be quite satisfactory. Single sideband or video modulation should not be attempted because operation would be completely unacceptable if transmitted through a frequency multiplier.

Varactor Temperature Characteristics

The design of varactor units has been carefully considered, and convenient engineering and packaging are usually available. These units are frequently mounted in such a way that the I^2R heat is carried off by thermal conduction to varactor mounts or other circuitry. In those cases where the associated circuitry cannot be used as a heat sink, cooling fins should be provided to help control hot spot temperatures. Most diodes are constructed of silicon wafers with excellent thermal characteristics and can therefore be expected to operate well in any environment suitable for semiconductors.

Over-all efficiencies of the varactors themselves in circuits such as that in Fig. 8-7 have been shown to degrade only 1 to 2 per cent when subjected to temperature variations greater than 100°C. The associated tuned circuits, on the other hand, frequently shift tuning sufficiently with a change in temperature to cause the over-all efficiency to fall off as much as 5 per cent. In normal operation, a temperature variation of 100°C without recourse to retuning is seldom encountered.

Varactor Noise Performance

The major amount of work with varactors has been at frequencies in the 2000 and 8000 MHz region. Some work has been done at lower frequencies (below 1000 MHz) in the transmitter field, but transmitters do not ordinarily suffer from noise limitations.

In the 2000 to 8000 MHz region, varactor multiplier units have been used as local oscillators in fixed frequency superheterodyne receivers. In these applications, varactor harmonic generators have proved to have less noise than the reflex klystrons normally used.

When such generators are used as local oscillators for receivers, care must be taken in the circuit design to avoid injection of noise through connecting leads to the receiver circuits.

Transmission Lines

Many different types of transmission lines are used in radio work, and all may be considered modifications of a two-wire spaced line. The length of a transmission line and the termination or load fed by the line have a considerable effect on the wave conducted by the line. If a line infinitely long could be constructed, the transmitted wave would be carried onward forever (assuming no loss of energy due to radiation, resistance, or leakage). The voltage would be determined by the potential applied and the loss in the line between the point of measurement and the source of the voltage. Of prime importance in an infinite line is that there should be only one wave traveling along the line and that it should travel outward from the source. An infinite line with only one wave is referred to as a nonresonant line. Any line of finite length that is terminated so as to produce no reflections is also called a nonresonant line.

When a transmission line has a definite, measurable length, the wave motion will be affected by the manner in which the line is terminated. Consider a transmission line that is a number of wavelengths long and terminated in an open circuit. When the wave traveling along the line reaches the end, the open circuit will act much like a mirror and reflect the wave back on itself. This reflected wave is actually a continuation of the incident wave, so that two traveling waves will exist on the line simultaneously. The resultant composite wave can be measured for both amplitude and wavelength. This resultant wave is called a *standing wave* because its nodes and maxima remain at the same point along the line. Since the incident and reflected waves travel at the same speed but in opposite directions, the amplitude of the standing wave at any point is continuously changing. The nodes and maxima do not travel along the line, however, as they do in incident and reflected waves.

Every transmission line — whether two-wire, coaxial, or waveguide — will have a certain *characteristic impedance*. This impedance is constant for each type of line and is determined by the size of the conductors, their spacing, and the type of dielectric between them. Although there are no conductors in the usual sense in a section of waveguide, the waveguide still has a characteristic impedance.

The characteristic impedance is usually referred to as Z_o and can be calculated from the formula:

$$Z_o = \sqrt{(R + J\omega L)/(G + J\omega C)} \qquad (49)$$

in which:

Z_o = characteristic impedance, in ohms
L = line inductance, in henrys per unit length
C = line capacitance, in farads per unit length
R = line resistance, in ohms per unit length
G = dielectric conductance, in mhos per unit length

Transmission lines are generally grouped into five categories as follows:

(1) Two-wire line
(2) Four-wire line
(3) Shielded pair
(4) Concentric or coaxial cable
(5) Waveguide.

A few other types of transmission line are sometimes used, but in most cases they require special construction techniques and have limited use.

Two-Wire Line

The two-wire line — the oldest and simplest form of transmission line — has been used at all frequencies from d-c to the lower microwave frequencies. It consists of two parallel wires or metallic tubes uniformly spaced at a distance less than an operating wavelength by means of insulators or spreaders. As can be seen from Eq. 49, the characteristic impedance, Z_o, of a transmission line is a function of its distributed inductance and capacitance. Therefore, an increase in the spacing of the wires will reduce the capacitance, causing an increase in the characteristic impedance. A reduction in the diameter of the wires will also have the effect of increasing Z_o.

For open-wire lines, in which the dielectric material between the wires is air, the value of Z_o may be found from the formula:

$$Z_o = 276 \, log_{10} \frac{2 D}{d} \qquad (50)$$

in which:

D = distance between centers of the wires
d = diameter of the wires

This formula is sufficiently accurate to be useful in calculating Z_o for lines to be used at frequencies up to about 30 MHz. Above this frequency, the radiation losses are usually too great for all but the shortest two-wire lines.

Four-Wire Line

The four-wire line is usually just a pair of two-wire lines with the wires uniformly spaced. These lines have the advantage of substantially reduced radiation with less mutual coupling to adjacent lines when diagonally opposite wires are connected in parallel.

Shielded Pair

A shielded pair consists of two conductors insulated from each other by a formed polyethylene cover. These pairs are maintained in a uniform twist by two fiberglass-reinforced foam polyethylene fillers. Over this are applied two helically wrapped copper shielding tapes, oppositely wound.

Because of its manner of construction, the shielded pair has an outstanding advantage in the high degree of balance-to-ground obtained. Radiation from a well shielded and balanced line such as this is virtually nonexistent when the current flow in each conductor is equal and opposite.

One form of shielded pair has come to be called *video pair* because it was originally designed specifically for short distance transmission of video signals in the frequency range from 1 to 5 MHz. This type of cable becomes important to the microwave engineer because it is frequently used to carry baseband information to the microwave transmitter when the transmitter is located a mile or two from the TV or telephone multiplex equipment.

Figure 8-8 is a graph showing typical attenuation values per mile from 100 Hz to 10 MHz. Since video pairs are balanced and shielded, they have a distinct advantage over unbalanced lines (such as coaxial cables) in the lower frequency range because of their extremely low crosstalk and noise pickup from external sources.

When used in this frequency range (100 Hz to 10 MHz), each video pair is effectively shielded against external pickup of a capacitive nature by the helically wrapped shields, and any magnetic interference is "balanced out" or neutralized because it has equal magnitude and angle in both conductors. A coaxial cable, on the other hand, is an unbalanced line with the shield also serving as the return conductor. This construction permits considerable noise pickup from external interference in the low and medium frequency ranges. It is only in the higher frequency ranges (hundreds or thousands of MHz) that the shielding of coaxial cables has its greatest use.

Coaxial Cable

Coaxial cable is constructed by surrounding one conductor with a second, which is at ground potential. In this manner, the radiation loss at higher frequencies is practically eliminated.

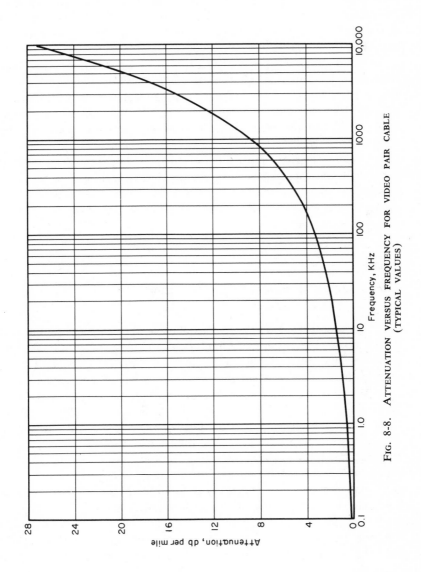

Fig. 8-8. Attenuation versus frequency for video pair cable (TYPICAL VALUES)

There are two main types of coaxial cable in common use today: (1) flexible and (2) rigid construction. In flexible cables, dielectric materials such as Mylar, polyethylene and, in a few cases, rubber are used to separate the inner and outer conductors. These cables have the advantage of relatively small size and can be easily installed by simply lacing them to a cable run. In most cases, however, they have higher attenuation and age much more rapidly than rigid line when exposed to the weather. Rigid coaxial lines use a solid outer tube rather than a flexible braid, and the inner conductor is held in place by uniformly spaced insulators. Since moisture increases dielectric losses, rigid coaxial lines are usually sealed at the joints; after being carefully dried, they are frequently pressurized with dry air or nitrogen to prevent the entrance of moisture-laden air.

The characteristic impedance of coaxial line varies with its distributed inductance and capacitance and therefore, just as with other types of lines, with the size and diameters of the conductors. For air-filled coaxial lines, the characteristic impedance, Z_o, may be found by the formula:

$$Z_o = 138 \, log_{10} \left(\frac{b}{a} \right) \tag{51}$$

in which:

b = "inside" diameter of outer conductor
a = "outside" diameter of inner conductor

For most types and sizes of coaxial cable, the characteristic impedance will be found to fall between the limits of 40 and 80 ohms. The total attenuation contributed by a coaxial line is composed of two components: the resistance of the conductors themselves and the losses in the dielectric.

In a coaxial cable, the electric lines of force are normal to the surface of the inner conductor. The electric field is made continuous by the presence of the two conductors, so that the lines of force in the space between the conductors are perpendicular to the direction of flow or propagation. On the other hand, the magnetic lines form closed paths around the inner conductor and are also perpendicular to the direction of propagation. Such a field configuration is called *transverse electromagnetic* (TEM), since both fields are everywhere normal to the direction of propagation. The TEM wave is the fundamental form of field configuration in all transmission lines, with the exception of waveguides, and is commonly called the principal mode of operation. Higher modes of operation may exist in a coaxial cable if the mean diameter of the cable exceeds the free space wavelength, but these waves are usually highly attenuated and normally cannot be propagated over a distance of any considerable length.

There is only one conductor in a waveguide and consequently no closed physical path through which the field energy may be returned. In this case, the lines of force must form continuous loops within the guide itself, and since the electric and magnetic fields are always perpendicular to each other, one of the fields must travel part of the time in the same direction as the propagation. Therefore, both fields cannot remain transverse to the propagating direction at the same time, and a TEM mode is impossible.

Waveguide

A waveguide may be generally defined as a structure — consisting of either a conductor or a dielectric or both — that can fully contain a propagated wave within its bounds. It is similar in action to wire transmission lines in that it is used to transmit RF energy from one place to another. It is at this point that the likeness to wire lines stops, since a waveguide consists of only one hollow metal tube or pipe. A waveguide is commonly formed in either a rectangular or circular cross section, although occasionally it may be elliptical, corrugated, or flexible for special purposes.

The fundamental reason for using a hollow waveguide is that the loss is lower than for either open-wire or coaxial lines at frequencies for which the waveguide is practical. Generally, waveguide is not used at frequencies below 2000 MHz. When power loss is more important than cost, however, it has sometimes been used at frequencies as low as 450 MHz. A second important reason for using waveguide is its power handling capability. It can transmit considerably more power than a coaxial line of the same size. The maximum power, P, of which a coaxial line is capable is given by the formula:

$$P = V^2/Z_o \qquad (52)$$

in which:

V = voltage
Z_o = characteristic impedance

From this it can be seen that to increase the power on the coaxial line you must increase the voltage. If the voltage is raised too high, the dielectric will break down and an arc will result. The breakdown path of the coaxial line is the distance from the outer conductor to the surface of the inner conductor. This distance is less than half the voltage breakdown distance in a round waveguide of the same size, since when operating in the principal mode, the maximum voltage in a round waveguide appears across its diameter.

Waveguide Modes

When Maxwell's equations are solved subject to boundary conditions imposed by perfectly conducting walls, it can be shown that any given guide can propagate an infinite number of different types of electromagnetic waves. Each type or mode has its own individual electric and magnetic field configuration. Each mode of operation also has a critical frequency below which it will not be propagated through a given size or guide. The critical, or cutoff, frequency, F_c, for any particular mode and the corresponding free-space wavelength, or cutoff, λ_c, are related by the formula:

$$\lambda_c = \frac{C}{F_c} \tag{53}$$

in which C is the free space velocity of light.

In a given size of waveguide, the mode with the lowest cutoff frequency is called the dominant or principal mode for that particular size of waveguide; it will be the only mode propagated if the frequency lies within the bounds of the cutoff frequency of the dominant mode and the cutoff frequency of the second lowest mode.

In most forms of waveguide, two types of mode are possible. The first is called the *transverse electric* (TE) since the field is everywhere perpendicular to the direction of propagation. TE waves are sometimes called *H*-plane waves since part of the magnetic field is parallel to the direction of propagation.

The second type of mode is called *transverse magnetic* (TM) since the magnetic field is everywhere perpendicular to the direction of propagation. TM waves have also been called *E*-plane waves because they have electric field components that are parallel to the direction of propagation.

The operating wavelength of a propagated wave is not the same in a waveguide as in space. It may be found from the equation:

$$\lambda_g = \frac{\lambda}{\sqrt{K_r}\ \sqrt{1-(\lambda/\lambda_c)^2}} \tag{54}$$

in which:

λ = free-space wavelength
λ_c = cutoff wavelength of a particular mode
K_r = dielectric constant of the material filling the guide (since most guides are air filled, K_r may be taken as unity)

The guide wavelength, λ_g, for all gas-filled waveguides is always larger than the corresponding wavelength in free space. This longer wavelength results from an apparent wave speed greater than the speed of light. Although this seems to violate the law of physics that says there can be no real velocity greater than that of light, the rate of energy flow in a guide — called *group velocity* (V_g) — is in reality always somewhat less than that of light and approaches zero when the free space wavelength approaches the cutoff value. The apparent contradiction results from a variation of field intensity

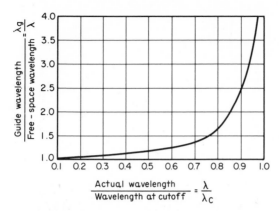

FIG. 8-9. VARIATION OF WAVELENGTH IN WAVEGUIDE WITH THE RATIO
OF ACTUAL WAVELENGTH TO CUTOFF WAVELENGTH

which, superimposed on the traveling wave, appears to move at a higher velocity.

The superimposed velocity of the change in field intensity is called *phase velocity* (V_p) and is related to the group velocity as follows:

$$V_g \times V_p = C^2 \tag{55}$$

in which C is the speed of light in free space. Now, since the point of maximum field intensity (not the actual energy) moves along the wave guide at the phase velocity, the apparent wavelength in a guide will always be longer than the wavelength in free space, as shown in Fig. 8-9.

The different modes also have different wavelengths in a guide, and it is usually impossible to make a guide that will be matched for more than one mode. In addition, any discontinuities such as corners or junctions will tend to excite other modes. Therefore, it is desirable to select a guide that will propagate only the lowest mode. If waveguide is selected in this manner, any mode generated beyond cutoff will die out within a very short distance of its source.

Rectangular Waveguide

The lowest mode or dominant mode in rectangular waveguide is the TE $_{1,0}$ mode. A simulated pattern of the field in the $TE_{1,0}$ mode is shown in Fig. 8-10, as well as a few of the other more common modes.

The electric field here is represented by electric lines of force that extend from the bottom to the top of the guide, with the intensity of the field varying sinusoidally along the long dimension, A. At the same time the field along the short dimension, B, is uniform. The magnetic field, always perpendicular

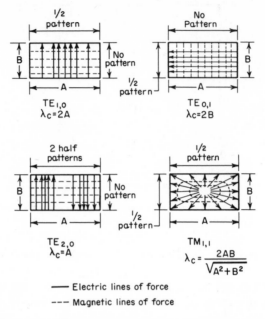

Fig. 8-10.   Waveguides modes for rectangular guide

to the electric lines of force, is also present (shown by the dashed lines). When the electric field is known, the magnetic field configuration can always be determined, and for the $TE_{1,0}$ mode, the magnetic lines form plain loops that are perpendicular to the electric lines.

In rectangular waveguide the cutoff wavelength for the dominant mode ($TE_{1,0}$) when filled with air is $\lambda_c = 2A$, in which A is the long dimension.

The various modes of any waveguide are designated by subscript numbers.[1] For example, the first subscript of a $TE_{1,0}$ or a $TM_{1,0}$ mode refers to the number of *half-cycle* variations in the fields along the long, or A, dimension. The second subscript number refers to the number of half-cycle variations along the short, or B, dimension.

Of prime importance in the practical application of waveguides is attenuation. In waveguides, attenuation is the result of two different factors: (1) the losses in the conducting walls of the waveguide, and (2) the attenuation or shunting effect of the dielectric material filling the guide. For dry air, in which the conductivity of the dielectric material may be ignored, the attenuation, a, developed in the rectangular waveguide is given by:

$$a = \frac{0.104B^{-1} + 0.52\,\lambda^2\,A^{-3}}{\sqrt{\lambda}\,\sqrt{1 - 0.25\,\lambda^2\,A^{-3}}} \qquad (56)$$

[1]Terman, F. E., *Electronic and Radio Engineering,* 4th ed., McGraw-Hill, pp. 135-136.

in which:

λ = free space wavelength
B = short dimension
A = long dimension

Circular Waveguide

Another form of waveguide has the geometrical configuration of a pipe and is called circular waveguide. The dominant mode of this form of guide is the $TE_{1,1}$ mode, which is the circular waveguide equivalent of the rectangular $TE_{1,0}$ mode. The cutoff wavelength of this mode is given by

$$\lambda_c = 1.71d \qquad (57)$$

in which d equals the inside diameter of the guide.

The cutoff wavelength of the higher modes in circular guides is quite complex and cannot be easily expressed in terms readily remembered, since they involve roots of Bessel functions. Circular waveguides have the disadvantage of having a very narrow range between the cutoff wavelength of the dominant mode and the next higher mode. For this reason, the frequency range over which pure mode operation is assured is relatively limited. In addition, because of its circular configuration, this guide does not have a characteristic that will positively prevent the plane of polarization of the wave from rotating around the guide axis as the wave is propagated. As a result, circular waveguide is used only for special circumstances, such as when a rotating joint is required.

Filters

The use of LC type low-pass, high-pass, and band-pass filters at lower frequencies is a familiar science. At microwave frequencies filters are also required, but they are of a different type. Waveguides with physical dimensions that will support only the dominant mode are in reality a form of band-pass filter. To have more sharply delineated characteristics for use at microwave frequencies, however, a combination of resonant sections or cavities is usually required.

Sections of waveguides are often formed into cavities by the simple expedient of putting a metal divider at the appropriate point in the guide, as shown in Fig. 8-11. The theory and details of design are covered extensively in other works.[1]

A single-cavity, such as that shown in Fig. 8-11, does not have the flat response and steep skirts normally required for microwave frequency separation. But when a series of cavities are coupled together and properly

---

[1] *Radiation Lab Series*, vol. 9, McGraw-Hill Book Co., Chaps. 9 and 10.

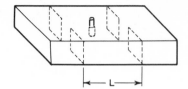

FIG. 8-11.　SINGLE WAVEGUIDE FILTER SECTION

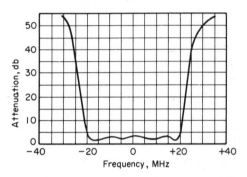

FIG. 8-12.　RESPONSE CURVE OF A TYPICAL MULTI-CAVITY FILTER

tuned, a response such as that shown in Fig. 8-12 is possible. The spacing between sections is usually an odd multiple of quarter wavelengths in order to couple effectively into each section and, at the same time, hold to a minimum undersirable interaction between cavities.

Theoretically, as the number of cavities increase, the skirts of the filter become steeper and the pass-band becomes flatter. In practice, however, the insertion loss increases, and the attenuation out of band tends to flatten off as a result of leakage around tuning screws and coupling flanges.

When tuning waveguide filters, one usually makes reflection measurements rather than transmission measurements. Reflection measurements are more easily obtained experimentally because the standing wave ratio does not depend on uniform input power at all frequencies. A typical setup for tuning waveguide filters is shown in Fig. 8-13. Here the filter is first completely detuned and the generator is set to the desired frequency. Next, the probe is moved along the slotted line until a maximum indication is obtained on the VSWR meter as close as possible to the generator end of the slot, indicating the presence of a high standing wave. The first cavity is then tuned for a near-minimum indication.

The probe is then moved toward the filter until the next maximum reading is obtained, and the second cavity is adjusted for a near-minimum. This process is repeated for each cavity in the filter until all cavities have been tuned. When the last cavity is tuned in this manner, the only power reflected will be from the resistive termination. To assure proper adjustment

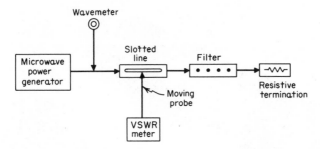

FIG. 8-13. TYPICAL FILTER TUNING HOOK-UP

of the pass-band of the filter, these measurements should then be repeated as described at the upper and lower limits of the pass-band.

If waveguide filters are to perform their desired functions, they must be properly terminated. The termination may take many forms and is very important to proper performance.

Isolators

An *isolator* is a device designed specifically to allow power transmission in only one direction. With performance of this type, it becomes very effective in avoiding problems from reflections that cannot be avoided in long waveguide runs.

An isolator is sometimes called a *load isolator* and is composed of a section of waveguide that contains a small piece of ferrite material under the influence of a strong magnetic field. A typical ferrite isolator is shown in Fig. 8-14. The piece of ferrite material may be considered to be a parasitically excited radiator of high efficiency, capable of transmitting RF energy in only one direction because of the influence of the magnetic field.

These devices usually have a rather wide bandwidth and require no tuning. The transmission losses are quite low — in the order of 0.1 to 0.5 db — in the conducting direction but as high as 20 to 30 db in the reverse, or nonconducting direction.

Duplexers

A *duplexer* (sometimes also called a *diplexer)* is a device used to connect more than one microwave transmitter or receiver to a single antenna or waveguide run. These devices are available in two types, one frequency-selective and the other strictly a wideband coupler.

The type that is frequency-selective is usually a combination of band-pass filters designed to couple to a single feed line, as shown in Fig. 8-15.

FIG. 8-14. TYPICAL FERRITE ISOLATORS (AT TOP, FOR USE WITH COAXIAL CABLE; AT BOTTOM, FOR USE WITH WAVEGUIDE)

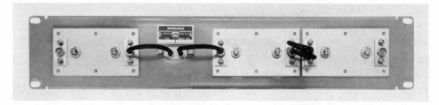

FIG. 8-15. BUDELMAN ANTENNA DUPLEXER FOR SYSTEMS EMPLOYING COAXIAL CABLE

This form of duplexer must be properly tuned to the desired frequencies of operation, and any unused waveguide ports or outputs must be terminated in a resistive load.

The wideband form of duplexer is a ferrite device operating on the general principles of the load isolator; it is called a *circulator* (see Fig. 8-16). RF energy entering this device is caused to rotate in a circle under the influence of two strong magnetic fields. The energy continues to rotate past the various ports in the unit until it finds one that provides a termination, either resistive or reactive. The losses will be cumulative and will usually amount to approximately 0.5 db per port.

Unused ports of a ferrite circulator normally should not be terminated;

FIG. 8-16. CIRCULATORS IN USE IN MICROWAVE TERMINAL

they should be either capped to provide a good reflection or left open. It is usually best to cap the unused ports to provide a better and more uniform reflection.

TWT Amplifiers

The general features in the construction of a *traveling-wave tube* are shown in Fig. 8-17. In this tube an electron gun similar to the type used in a klystron generates a pencil-like beam having a rather high velocity and typically corresponding to an accelerating voltage in the order of 1500 V. The beam passes through a long, loosely wound helix and then is collected by an electrode at the far end of the tube. The evacuated envelope, with the helix

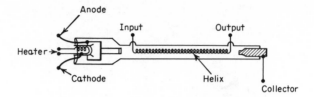

FIG. 8-17   TRAVELING-WAVE TUBE

inside, is immersed in an axial magnetic field to prevent the beam from spreading as it proceeds along the center of the helix.

The signal to be amplified is applied to the helix at the end adjacent to the electron gun. Then, if the accelerating voltage is appropriately adjusted to cause the electrons to propagate synchronously along the helix with the input wave, an amplified signal can be taken from the end of the helix nearest the collector electrode.

The process by which amplification is obtained may be described as follows. The signal applied at the input propagates around the turns of the helix, producing an electric field at the center. It is directed axially with the helix and concentric with the electron beam. If the frequency is above a particular value, it will propagate along the helix at approximately the speed of light. The axial electric field due to the input signal will advance with a velocity that is very close to the speed of light multiplied by the ratio of helix pitch to helix circumference. Then, when the electron acceleration voltages are adjusted so that the velocity of the electrons traveling through the helix approximates the rate of advance of the axial field, an interaction takes place that results in energy being given to the wave on the helix, producing amplification.

The TWT amplifier has two important advantages. The first is the extremely large bandwidth attainable at the higher microwave frequencies, and the second is the very low noise factor available from tubes designed for use in preamplifiers. The chief limitation of bandwidth is the difficulty encountered in matching the input and output lines over a wide frequency range. Available tubes have bandwidths approaching one octave. The chief limitation in the noise figure reduction lies in the dispersion of the electron beam as it propagates through the helix. Electron beam spread results in some of the electrons' being collected by the helix, introducing noise in the signal.

Diversity Combiners

Diversity combiners allow two or more sets of radio equipment to operate in a single baseband system. They frequently have the ability to supply the same input signal to two or more transmitters. The combiner in

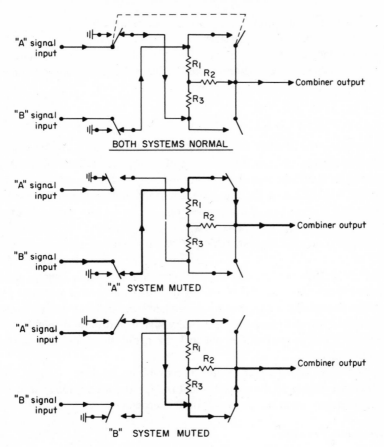

FIG. 8-18. TYPICAL DIVERSITY COMBINER CIRCUIT

its simplest form takes advantage of the 3- to 6-db increase in signal-to-noise ratio that is available when the same information is carried by two channels. Figure 8-18 is a schematic that will aid in understanding the operation of a combiner circuit. Combining of the received signals is accomplished in the resistive network, which receives two signals of equal amplitude at inputs A and B. The level at the output of the combiner is the same as the level of either signal as long as both are in phase.

Considered individually, each signal would normally experience a 6-db loss through the network. Since both signals are in phase, however, they add on a voltage basis according to the expression:

$$20 \, log \left(\frac{E_1}{E_2} \right) \tag{58}$$

This voltage addition results in a 6-db increase, which just compensates for the loss in the resistive network.

Frequency components associated with noise, however, are completely random and therefore are never in phase. The amplitude addition from combining signals of this type will be found to equal

$$10 \, log \left(\frac{P_1}{P_2} \right) \tag{59}$$

and therefore the addition will be only 3 db. From this it can be seen that when two signals, each in the presence of noise, are added in this manner, there will be a net increase of signal-to-noise ratio of 3 db over what is to be expected from either of the input signals individually. When the signal-to-noise ratios are unequal, the improvement will be greater than this up to a value of 6 db over the worst channels.

In most actual cases, switching is also provided to remove one or the other of the signals when the signal-to-noise ratio exceeds some predetermined value, thus precluding the possibility of a badly faded signal actually introducing severe noise. When one or the other microwave systems fails or becomes excessively noisy, a relay disconnects the bad equipment from the combining network, grounding the faulty signal and other contacts on the same relay bridge across the network to avoid the 6-db loss normally encountered.

There are many other means of combining multiple signals. Some methods are highly sophisticated, but the type described above is the one most commonly used on point-to-point microwave.

Microwave Terminals

A basic microwave terminal consists of a transmitter and a receiver, arranged for full duplex operation, plus an antenna system, as illustrated in Fig. 8-19. In many systems, standby equipment is provided and is automatically switched into service when the primary equipment fails. Recently

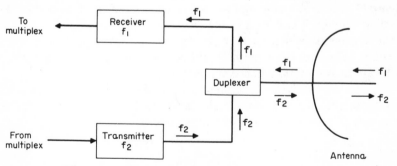

Fig. 8-19. Block diagram of microwave terminal

Fig. 8-20.   Tube type 6000-MHz
Band Microwave Terminal

Fig. 8-21.   Tube type 6000-MHz
Band Microwave Terminal with
Hot Standby

developed solid state microwave equipment is claimed to be so reliable that standby equipment is not required for many applications. Solid state equipment offered by at least one manufacturer is so compact that a complete terminal does not fill 8½ inches of rack space. Typical microwave terminals are shown in Figs. 8-20, 8-21, and 8-22.

Microwave Repeaters

Several types of microwave repeaters are available. Figure 8-23 is a block diagram of a *back-to-back repeater* in which the video (composite multiplex) signal is fed from the output of a receiver to the input of its associated transmitter.

A block diagram of a *feedback type repeater* is given in Fig. 8-24. One

FIG. 8-22　SOLID-STATE MICROWAVE TERMINAL WITH STANDBY

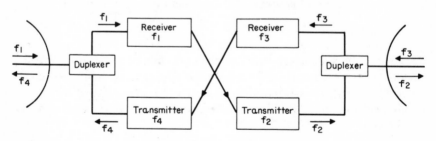

FIG. 8-23.　BACK-TO-BACK REPEATER

feature of this type of repeater is that the frequency of the repeaters is automatically locked to a terminal transmitting frequency.

Heterodyne repeaters are becoming increasingly popular in long-haul systems. As shown in Fig. 8-25, the signal is not demodulated but is instead passed through a down-converter, amplified at a relatively low frequency (usually 70 MHz), and then passed through an up-converter.

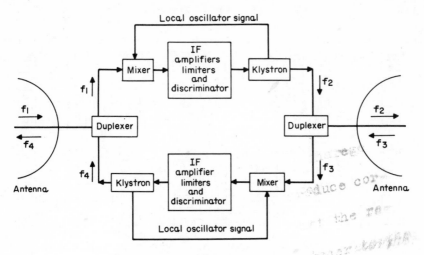

FIG. 8-24. DUPLEX FEEDBACK REPEATER

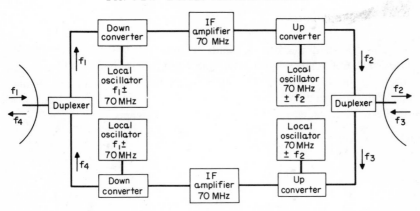

FIG. 8-25. HETERODYNE REPEATER

Typical Systems

Most private microwave systems provide two transmission paths, one in each direction for full duplex operation, as shown in Fig. 8-26. Common carrier systems may have several transmission stacked paths (Fig. 8-27).

FIG. 8-26. TYPICAL PRIVATE MICROWAVE SYSTEM PROVIDING ONE MICROWAVE PATH IN EACH DIRECTION

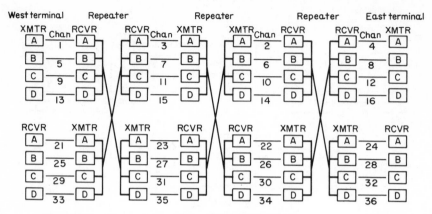

FIG. 8-27.　MICROWAVE SIGNAL PATHS EMPLOYED IN SOME CARRIER SYSTEMS

Operating Frequencies

The so-called microwave bands include the 960-MHz, 2000-MHz, 4000-MHz, 6000-MHz, 8500-MHz, and 12,000-MHz bands. At the present time, only the 952- to 960-MHz band is divided into authorized channels specifically assigned to licensees. In the other bands, specific frequencies are selected and requested by station license applicants.

9

Microwave Path Engineering

Having previously selected a type of microwave equipment with the desired operating characteristics, a particular power output, and a receiver with a specified signal sensitivity, the microwave path engineer faces the problem of providing a received signal level that will guarantee reliable service over the path selected.

When engineering a microwave path, the first step is to select the most direct route between the points to be joined. This route should then be broken into sections between 25 and 35 miles in length to determine the approximate number of repeaters required.

Once the approximate route has been determined, the following considerations are necessary to provide the required receiver input power:

(1) Transmitter output power
(2) Transmit and receive antenna gains
(3) Individual path losses
(4) Transmission line and connector losses
(5) Diplexer or circulator losses
(6) Signal power required at the receiver input.

Although these are the major items of importance to the operation, there are many more that tend to complicate the engineering. Following a final route selection, a computation of expected fade margin and performance should be made for each hop of the proposed route.

119

Path Selection

The location of repeaters and, in particular, of antennas will depend upon local terrain as well as the character of the area, whether urban or rural. Each location has its own peculiar requirements that will affect the route selected in varying ways.

Since the elevation of antennas is essential to adequate clearance, advantage should be taken of available rooftops whenever possible. By placing antennas on the tops of high buildings, the need for high towers can be greatly reduced.

Since microwave repeaters are often located in sparsely populated areas, consideration must be given to year-round accessibility. Also, whenever it is economically and topographically possible, paths over large bodies of water or through river valleys should be avoided. Access roads that are expensive and hard to maintain may be avoided by obtaining sites close to existing roads and highways. Proximity to airways around an airport will require special tower construction standards and limitations as outlined by the FAA or similar aeronautical authority.

Approximate Repeater Location

The careful use of topographical and ordinary road maps will assist considerably in choosing repeater locations. Whenever possible, alternative sites should be selected and included in the initial planning study. These alternative sites should be suitable for integration into the system should the prime site be unobtainable or inaccessible. In mountainous country, selection of sites purely from the standpoint of maximum transmission can often result in the choice of a site whose elevation makes it practically inaccessible. The advantages of such a location are frequently nullified by economic considerations, bearing in mind that a year-round access road is necessary for maintenance and construction. Even though many microwave relay stations will be unattended after construction, they still must be accessible all year.

In urban and suburban areas the local zoning laws should be carefully studied to avoid expensive delays at construction time. In other than rural areas (and occasionally even in rural areas) the required size of plot can affect selection.

The plot size required usually depends upon the type and height of the tower itself. A self-supporting tower must be constructed more sturdily than a guyed tower in order to resist wind loads. Guyed towers of equal height are more stable and usually less costly, but they also require larger plots of ground because of the spread of the guy wires. Figure 9-1 is a table for use in determining the minimum plot size required for guyed towers.

In making site selections, many microwave engineers prefer to choose a

Tower height	Guy ratio			
	80 per cent		100 per cent	
	A	B	A	B
100	135	156	165	191
110	147	170	180	208
120	159	184	195	225
125	165	191	203	234
130	171	198	210	243
140	183	211	225	260
150	195	225	240	277
160	207	239	255	294
170	219	253	270	312
175	225	260	278	320
180	231	267	285	329
190	243	281	300	346
200	255	294	315	364
210	267	308	330	381
220	279	322	345	398
225	285	329	353	407
230	291	336	360	416
240	303	350	375	433
250	315	364	390	450
260	327	378	405	468
270	339	391	420	484
280	351	405	435	502
290	363	419	450	519
300	375	433	465	536
310	387	447	480	554
320	399	461	495	572
325	405	467	503	580
330	411	475	510	588
340	423	488	525	606
350	435	502	540	623

FIG. 9-1. MINIMUM PLOT SIZES REQUIRED FOR GUYED TOWERS (THREE GUYS ASSUMED, 120 DEG APART)

Calculations:

$$A = 1.5 \ (GT + 10)$$
$$B = 1.73 \ (GT + 10)$$

in which A = short dimension of rectangular plot, in feet; B = long dimension of rectangular plot, in feet; G = guy ratio (ratio of tower height to lateral guy dimension); and T = tower height, in feet.

zigzag path in order to prevent problems from reflections or overshoot of the radio beam. Such problems can easily be avoided by placing the repeaters one-half to three-quarters of a mile on each side of the direct path. Overshoot is usually not a problem because of the curvature of the earth and other obstructions. But if it does occur, it can cause many sleepless nights. Every path engineer should keep in mind that free space losses increase only 6 db every time the distance is doubled, and an additional 6-db loss means relatively little to a receiver with a 30-db fade margin.

Number and Location of Repeaters

When the tentative path has been selected, it should be divided into sections of approximately equal length. If, after due consideration, the microwave beam must go over a large lake or body of water, this path should be considered a problem path and the repeater spacing reduced. When paths over water are unavoidable, it is best to put a repeater fairly close to one shore of the body of water and try to operate with the antenna as low as possible. This will usually cause any reflections from the water to pass over the receiving antenna altogether, thus reducing the cancellation effect and consequently the fading. Paths over water are covered in more detail in the section titled Over-Water Paths.

The number and final location of repeaters will depend considerably upon the results of the path survey. In general, those sections of the microwave route that are approximately the same length can be expected to have similar signal-to-noise performance.

Topography Analysis and Measurement

Among the various items required to make a path survey is a good set of maps of the entire area of the proposed route. It is advisable to have aeronautical charts as well as topographical maps showing elevation and contour lines. In addition, a good set of road maps showing primary and secondary roads will be helpful.

The proposed route should be checked against an aeronautical chart and if any antennas will be located in airways near airports, they should be discussed with aeronautical authorities. If such consultations do not take place at the time of the survey, the possible re-engineering required when the FCC checks the antenna location with the aeronautics authority may result in much added expense and lost time.

If the maps used are reasonably current, they can be depended on to be fairly accurate, and much path engineering can be taken care of right in the office. The only field trips necessary will be to check for man-made obstructions and trees that are not shown in the maps. High points indicated along a path should be checked against a known elevation such as a Coast and Geodetic Survey bench mark. If the only maps available are very old, the contour information can be off by as much as 200 to 300 ft, and accurate measurement of elevations will be required to assure proper clearance.

In order to make a satisfactory survey, the location of a known bench mark, a sensitive altimeter, and accurate maps are required. In addition, it is advisable to have a recording barograph for accurate measurement of atmospheric pressure while using the altimeter. The recording barograph is adjusted and set in operation before the altimeter is adjusted accurately at the known bench mark. The survey is started from this point of reference, and all elevation measurements should be corrected to agree with this elevation.

Altimeter recordings are made at accessible intervals along the path previously determined on the maps. It is important to record the altitude, temperature, and time of the reading at each point along the path. It should be kept in mind that altitude and temperature measurements should not be made in a moving or closed vehicle because serious errors may result.

When the path survey has been completed, the readings of the altimeter should be checked at the initial, or a succeeding, bench mark. If there is a discrepancy due to a change in atmospheric pressure, the readings must be corrected. When there are extreme weather changes during the survey, serious inaccuracies will often occur. Under these conditions it is better to abandon the survey and repeat it on another day rather than to try to make corrections for the rapidly changing temperature and pressure.

While making the survey it is advisable to note any obstructions along the path, especially at the higher elevations. Estimates of the height of trees and buildings are particularly important; such notations can be most conveniently made directly on the map.

It is advisable to plan the survey of a path so that it can be completed during the day. Also, it is best not to make altitude measurements and recordings early in the morning or late in the evening, since rapidly changing pressure and temperature conditions will often introduce substantial errors.

When the elevation measurements have been completed, they should be carefully plotted in a profile study, and any readings that appear to be in error should be taken a second time. The profile study will result in a site selection that can be considered final from an engineering standpoint.

There are many ways in which the profile can be plotted. The two most common are to put the various elevations on profile paper with four-thirds earth radius curvature lines or on rectangular coordinate paper above a common zero ordinate. The four-thirds earth radius paper is readily available, but paper for other curvatures will probably have to be made up.

The rectangular plot is by far the most convenient and also provides a more graphic presentation of the effect of changes in K. Figure 9-2 is a typical rectangular topographic profile on which the microwave beam centerline has been plotted. In making a plot of this type, an examination of the minimum and maximum elevations over the path should be made. These should be plotted in the manner shown.

Figure 9-3 is a template on which various conditions of K have been laid out. If such a template is used to determine antenna elevations, the profile plot should be made to the same vertical and horizontal scale as the template provides. It should be remembered in using a template of this type that care must be exercised to keep the horizontal grid lines of the two sheets parallel.

Once all of the repeater sites have been fixed and plots made of the paths, the next step is determining antenna heights. This step can be completed for each individual path before proceeding to the next, or in relatively flat country it can be quite effectively saved for a final step to be performed in the office. This study should also result in a reasonably accurate determination of the airline distance between repeater sites. Such information is required to determine path loss and antenna size for each hop.

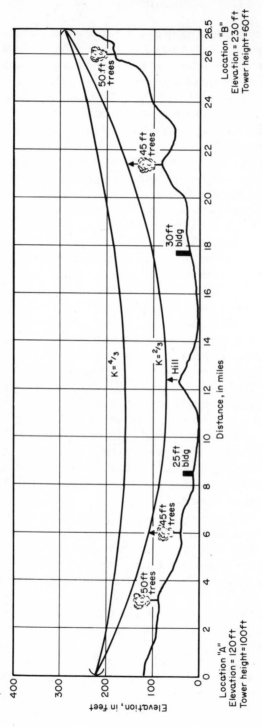

Fig. 9-2. TYPICAL RECTANGULAR TOPOGRAPHIC PROFILE

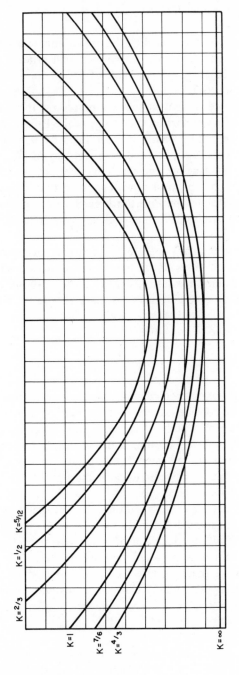

Fig. 9-3. Equivalent earth profile template

Scale: Each square = 100 ft vertically and 2 miles horizontally; or, each square = 400 ft vertically and 4 miles horizontally.

Determination of Antenna Height

The antenna height is determined by the operational criteria of the system as well as the terrain traversed. The operational criteria are used to determine path clearance (Fig. 4-5 is a table of acceptable standards commonly used for this purpose).

The actual clearance in feet at various points on the path may be critical and can be determined from a knowledge of the Fresnel zone dimension. The Fresnel zone radius should be multiplied by 0.3, 0.6, or some other value deemed acceptable. This value in feet should be added to the height of any possible obstruction, and a suitable mark made on the profile plot. The profile should then be marked with an indication of the microwave beam center line. If the plot is on four-thirds earth radius paper, the beam center line is simply a straight line just touching the indicated clearance marks.

If the plot is on rectangular paper, the appropriate curve for the proper value of K can be adjusted to just touch the clearance marks. The profile is then moved horizontally until the desired curve is at the optimum elevation at both the transmitting and receiving sites. A mark should be placed at this elevation to be used as a measure of the elevation of the antenna. (Be careful to keep the horizontal grid lines matched.)

Over-Water Paths

Due to the high reflection coefficient of water, each path that must cross a body of water must be considered as a problem path. When a microwave beam strikes the surface of a body of water, it will be reflected with very little attenuation. If the reflected portion of the signal can be intercepted by the receiving antenna and the reflection point lies at a point sufficiently removed from the center line of the beam to cause the signal to be 180 deg out of phase, severe cancellation will result.

As can be seen from Fig. 3-4, when the reflected signal approaches a distance equal to the even-number Fresnel zone (2-4-etc.), severe fading can result from the high reflection coefficient of water, and it becomes obvious that these paths must be handled in a different manner.

Optical tests indicate that, regardless of its original polarization, a reflected wave will have a predominance of horizontal polarization. Tests performed at microwave frequencies have indicated similar characteristics. For this reason, most path engineers take advantage of the loss due to cross polarization on paths over water.

The transmitting and receiving antennas are polarized vertically so that any reflected signal that arrives with a horizontal polarization will experience the cross polarization loss, which can be as great as 20 db. This added attenuation of the reflected signal will reduce the out-of-phase cancellation due to reflection of even-number Fresnel zone waves.

Although these methods are widely used, they are not always as effective as theory would indicate because of the dispersion of the signal at the reflecting surface. The surface of water is seldom calm, and frequently there are objects floating in it that make the polarization effect less than perfect. It has therefore become common practice, in addition to using vertical polarization, to install the antenna in such a manner that it is not possible for second zone reflections to reach it. This is usually accomplished by putting one of the antennas on an elevated tower and the other on one that is quite low. The towers are located so that one is fairly close to the body of water. It usually does not matter which antenna is near the water so long as any trees or large rocks are not obstructing the beam.

This high-low antenna configuration almost always results in a shorter hop, which has the further advantage of reduced space attenuation. Overwater hops should seldom be greater than 25 miles at frequencies above 1000 MHz unless the antenna near the body of water is quite low and is looking at an antenna that is very high, such as one on a mountain top. Even in this configuration a minimum fade margin of at least 1 db per mile should be permitted in lake areas in order to compensate for all the other effects present.

Having taken all precautions to assure minimum cancellation on overwater paths, the phenomenon known as ducting must be considered. As explained in Chap. 3, ducting is a condition in which the microwave beam becomes trapped between two layers of air with widely different refraction index.

Over swampy land, lakes, or other bodies of water, evaporation will cause a substantial increase in humidity. When this increased humidity is accompanied by periods of little or no wind, the air will stratify, and severe ducting conditions will occur daily during the summer months. When ducting is predominant, it is impossible to predict which way the beam will be conducted. Therefore little can be done to compensate for its effects. The only effective way to reduce the loss of signal due to ducting is to use an antenna with wide beam angle and a transmitter with substantial power output — and these measures, of course, defeat the purpose of using microwave in the first place.

When circumstances make it impossible to avoid over-water hops, they should be so engineered that the mean signal will be a minimum of 25 to 30 db above the receiver threshold 99.99 per cent of the time. This should be accomplished using antennas with a minimum beam width of 15 to 20 deg at the half-power points. If the hop can be satisfactorily engineered in this manner, the effects of reflection and ducting will rarely result in a complete outage.

Form for Tabulating Path Data

The most convenient method of determining system performance and establishing antenna size is to use a prepared form for tabulating path data. This form should be as complete as possible, giving all the information essential to any particular path. It is best to have one form for each path as a means to this end and to reduce confusion.

Path Calculations

There are several items of information needed to complete the path calculations that can either be obtained from the equipment manufacturer or independently calculated. This data — including receiver noise figures, receiver threshold, receiver IF bandwidth, and the level at which the receiver may overload — is required in order to determine the proper mean signal level and also the antenna size.

Some manufacturers provide a curve of receiver noise output versus RF power at the receiver input. If available, it will by-pass the rather long procedure of establishing the desired operating level from the required fade margin. The calculations are not particularly difficult, but care must be exercised to avoid errors. Some assumptions can be made that will introduce slight errors but are justified in the interest of brevity.

The purpose of the calculation is to determine the *receiver threshold*. The receiver threshold has been defined as the point at which the noise level equals the signal level. The noise, variously called *fluctuation noise* and *white noise,* can be considered to be equivalent to a uniform spectrum of energy spreading in frequency from zero to infinity, with random phase and timing.

Therefore, somewhere within this spectrum the receiver will accept a band of noise energy, the magnitude of which is dependent on the width of the band and the temperature of the noise source. The magnitude of the noise energy can be calculated from the formula:

$$N_t = 1.38 \times 10^{-23} \; TB \qquad\qquad (60)$$

in which:

N_t = available thermal noise power
T = temperature, in degrees Kelvin
B = bandwidth of the receiver or amplifier, in Hertz

The resistance of the antenna is not important to the available noise power, since it is assumed to be properly matched, but the temperature is important. For most microwave systems with antennas oriented a few degrees above the horizon, this temperature has been found to be approximately 300°K, which will equate to a noise power of −174 dbm per Hertz of bandwidth.

Typical microwave receivers have a bandwidth of approximately 10 MHz, and if the noise energy from each Hertz of this bandwidth is added, the total noise power will be increased by a factor of 70 db. Therefore, the noise power present at the input of a receiver with a 10 MHz bandwidth would be at a value of −104 dbm. Noise generated within the receiver's circuits will have the effect of further increasing the noise, thus decreasing the signal sensitivity.

Receiver-generated noise has a magnitude determined by circuit design and is commonly referred to as *receiver noise*. This noise will have a value equal to the receiver noise figure listed in the manufacturer's specification. For typical microwave receivers at the suggested bandwidth, the noise figure will be approximately 10 to 12 db. This noise must be added to the thermal noise power. A typical input noise value would be −92 dbm.

The addition of these noise powers tell us that an RF signal received at a level of −92 dbm will just equal the thermal and receiver noise and therefore would not be usable because it would be impossible for the discriminator to tell the difference between the two signal sources. It has previously been shown (in Fig. 5-13) that a discriminator will require an S/N ratio of 3 to 6 db before self-generated crosstalk and distortion are sufficiently suppressed. This figure must also be included in order to determine the receiver output noise threshold. With a noise level of −92 dbm, plus a discriminator threshold of 6 db, we see that a typical receiver output noise threshold is −86 dbm for a receiver with a 10 MHz bandwidth.

With a threshold of −86 dbm as the point at which the demodulated signal just starts to exceed the noise, the S/N ratio can be expected to improve db for db as the signal level is increased. Therefore, for a nondiversity system to stay above this figure 99.99 per cent of the time, we see that a margin of 38 db is required. This means that the design level of the received microwave signal should be −48 dbm at the input to the receiver exclusive of any losses due to waveguide, circulators, or combiners. Although this figure is adequate to prevent system fadeout 99.99 per cent of the time, the baseband signal-to-noise ratio may still be higher than desired as a result of noise being added to the baseband signal by video amplifier distortion. This noise will be dependent on the number and bandwidth of the information signals the system must carry and will add to the fluctuation noise caused by RF signal power. This subject was covered more completely in Chapter 6.

Antenna Size Selection

Having established an input signal level to be used, the path calculations and determination of the antenna size are most conveniently accomplished with the use of a prepared form such as that shown in Fig. 9-4. Almost any variation of this typical format can be used, but it should provide a complete record when finished. One sheet should be prepared for each path, and all information should be filled in, even when it requires duplication.

In order to demonstrate the advantages of this procedure, an explanation will be given for each step of the form. The heading information is taken from a knowledge of the location of the path. The latitude and longitude information can be obtained from the path maps and charts and will likely be that for the transmit station. The path length should be the airline distance from transmitter to receiver and can also be obtained from the maps and

---

	MICROWAVE PATH		

From: "A"	To: "B"
Type equipment: Model L-62	Frequency: 6 KHz
Location:	Lat: Long:
Elevation: 1300 ft	Tower height: 300 ft Type: Guyed
Profile No: #1	Path length: 26 miles

Losses		Gains	
(A) Path loss	141 db	(F) Transmit power	+30 dbm
(B) Waveguide loss	1.5 db	(G) Receive input	-40 dbm
(C) Circulator loss	1.5 db	(H) Total gains	70 db
(D) Other	3.0 db	(I) Required antenna gain	77 db
(E) Total	147 db		

Transmit		Receive	
Antenna height	30 ft	Antenna height	30 ft
Antenna size	6 ft	Antenna size	6 ft
Antenna gain	39.0 db	Antenna gain	39.0
Reflector height	230	Reflector height	230
Reflector size	8×12 ft	Reflector size	8×12 ft
Reflector gain	0	Reflector gain	0

Mean receiver signal	-40 dbm
Carrier to noise	46 db
Fade margin	40 db

Remarks:

FIG. 9-4. PREPARED FORM FOR TABULATING PATH DATA

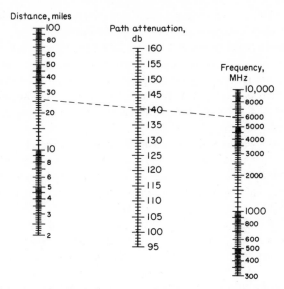

FIG. 9-5. FREE-SPACE ATTENUATION BETWEEN ISOTROPIC ANTENNAS

EIA	WR284	WR187	WR137	WR112	WR90	WR75	WR62		
								Coax RG58	Coax RG8U
JAN	RG48U	RG49U	RG50U	RG51U	RG52U		RG91U		
Outside Dimensions, inches	3 × 1.5	2 × 1	1.5 × 0.75	1.25 × 0.625	1 × 0.5	0.85 × 0.475	0.702 × 0.391		
Cutoff frequency, GHz	2.6 to 3.95	3.95 to 5.85	5.85 to 8.2	7.05 to 10.0	8.2 to 12.4	10.0 to 15.0	12.4 to 18.0		
2 GHz								34	13
3 GHz	.9							45	17
4 GHz		2.2						54	21
5 GHz		1.6						63	25
6 GHz			2.9					72	29
7 GHz			2.6					82	32
8 GHz				3.6					
9 GHz				3.4	5.8				
10 GHz				3.2	5.2	7.4			
11 GHz					4.8	6.6			
12 GHz					4.6	6.0			
13 GHz						5.8	9.2		
14 GHz						5.5	8.7		
15 GHz						5.3	7.9		

(left axis: Attenuation per 100 feet, db)

FIG. 9-6. ATTENUATION IN OXYGEN-FREE, HIGH CONDUCTIVITY COPPER WAVEGUIDE
Attenuation varies with different types of waveguide materials.

charts. The profile number is assigned from the profile chart, which should be attached to this form as a part òf the permanent record.

The losses should be entered in their appropriate box. Space loss can be obtained from Fig. 9-5 and attenuation for a typical copper waveguide from Fig. 9-6. The circulator or diplexer loss should be taken from manufacturers' information. The losses shown on Fig. 9-4 as "other" consist of minor losses such as those at flanges, elbows, and gas dams and other similar kinds of equipment that can add attenuation.

The gains listed are due to transmitter power and receiver input. In the case illustrated, the transmitter is a 1-watt system, which equals +30 dbm. Receiver input is either a calculated value determined from receiver threshold or a value taken from manufacturers' specifications for the design value of input power.

The "required antenna gain" is a figure obtained by subtracting total gains from total losses. This is the gain required of the transmit and receive antenna and can be divided equally or unequally at the discretion of the engineer.

The antenna gain shown in Fig. 9-4 is the gain taken from Fig. 7-6. In this care, a 6-ft antenna at 6 GHz gives a gain of 39 db; these figures are entered in both the transmit and receive portions of the form. The antenna in question is mounted at the base of a tower and focused on a reflector elevated on the tower. Since the reflector gain is here taken to be zero, the antenna gain is that shown in Fig. 7-6. The reflector height is che height above ground when the proper antenna-to-reflector separation has been achieved.

The mean receiver signal is the design value shown in (G) under gains. When this value is subtracted from the threshold figure of −86 dbm (as previously calculated or taken from manufacturers' specifications), it will give the carrier-to-noise value of −46 db.

The fade margin is the amount by which the signal can fade before the receiver output noise from all sources goes beyond tolerable values. This figure will have to come from manufacturers' charts or previous experience with the equipment. It can be calculated, but the process is extremely involved. The reader is referred to *National Bureau of Standards Technical Note 100*. When such calculations are performed, nearly all available data is based on a single-tone steady-state load and will thus give only approximate results.

10

Antenna Orientation and System Measurement

In order to assure that the highly directional microwave antenna is properly oriented, it is advisable to make careful measurements of the received RF signal strength as the antenna orientation is varied. The antennas should be aimed so that the transmitting and receiving signal lies in the middle of the large main lobe of the antenna pattern. Ordinarily this can be accomplished by swinging the antenna from side to side while noting the angles of the half-power points, then fixing the antenna halfway between these two angles. The same measurements should be made in the vertical direction, being careful to avoid ground reflection problems.

Signal Strength Measurements

The strength of the received signal can be measured accurately with the aid of a measuring instrument specifically designed for the purpose. The received power reading can be taken directly from the meters on the instrument, and no further effort is necessary. Sometimes, however, a suitable meter is not available. In such circumstances the microwave receiver itself can be used as a satisfactory measuring instrument if it is applied carefully. All good microwave receivers are equipped with an AGC (automatic gain control) system or a series of limiters that compensate for varying propagation conditions and keep the proper signal level at the discriminator or detector. If properly used, these circuits can be temporarily equipped to provide a satisfactory indication of the received RF energy. Either the AGC bus or the first limiter is capable of providing the necessary signal strength information.

When the receiver is equipped with an AGC system, a high impedance DC-VTVM should be connected between the distribution bus and ground. This bus will usually carry a d-c voltage that will vary between 0 and 5 volts depending on the strength of the received signal. In the event the receiver does not have an AGC system, the DC-VTVM should be connected to the first limiter of the receiver. The d-c bias voltage of the limiter will be found to increase with increased signal level. Note, however, that care must be exercised to be certain this connection is made to the first limiter, since this is the only limiter that can be used as an indicator of received signal power.

It immediately becomes apparent that these meter readings will bear relatively little information about signal strength unless some calibrating measurements are made first. The necessity for accurate calibration of the receiver can be avoided by placing a variable RF antennuator between the antenna feed line and the receiver input, as shown in Fig. 10-1. This attenuator should be adjusted to give a loss of approximately 10 db to the received signal, and the measuring instrument should be set so that the meter comes to rest on any convenient reading. As the antenna orientation process proceeds and the strength of the received signal changes, the attenuator loss must be adjusted to maintain the meter indication as its original value. The changes in received signal level are then indicated by the variation of the attenuator loss, with the signal increasing as the loss increases and decreasing as the loss decreases.

In making most measurements of propagated signals, accuracy is more easily obtained by checking for signal nulls or dips. In the case of antenna orientation, this is not possible because the intent is to position the antennas so that the middle of the strong main lobe is along the center line of the path.

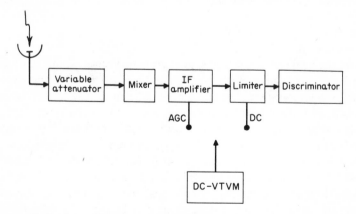

Fig. 10-1. Method of measuring received signal level variations

When adjusting for maxima, the best approach is to swing the antenna pattern to one side until the received signal strength is down by exactly 3 db, or one-half the power. The angle of the antenna should be marked at this point and the pattern swung back until the signal is down an equal amount on the opposite side. This angle is then measured, and the number of degrees between the two is the width of the lobe being measured. The antenna is then set halfway between the two half power angles. This procedure will also help to assure that the *main lobe* is located along the center line of the propagation path, an important consideration since only the main lobe has a beam width that approaches the value shown in published antenna information.

Parabolic Antenna Orientation

In starting the orientation, the parabola should first be located with its associated antenna and hardware at the proper elevation on the tower. The mounting hardware should be firmly affixed to the tower so final orientation can be accomplished with adjusting screws. The waveguide or coaxial cable should then be connected to the RF equipment. As a preliminary step, the parabola should be aimed as accurately as possible by sighting above the horizon and in the direction of the associated transmit or receive equipment.

It is best to make the final adjustment of the antenna on a signal receiving basis since communication with the man on the tower is simplified. The transmitter is equally important, of course, but usually it is sufficiently well pointed by preliminary sighting to get a signal to the receiver. Once the transmitted signal has been received and identified, the receiving antenna assembly should be swept horizontally for the maximum signal as previously described and then temporarily locked, preventing further horizontal motion. The antenna assembly should then be swept vertically for the maximum signal. When first sweeping the vertical direction, the antenna should be pointed perceptibly high, working the main lobe lower and lower toward the horizon until the maximum signal is obtained.

The main lobe should be swept through its maximum to the halfpower points on each side, and once these angles have been accurately determined, the antenna should be pointed halfway between these points and permanently locked. The receiver should then be returned to its normal configuration, the transmitter activated, and the measurement procedure repeated at the receiver of the next station.

For those installations that do not have a transmitter and a receiver at each site, it will be necessary to align the transmitting antenna (which was only roughly sited previously) before the VTVM connections and the attenuator are removed from the receiver. This process is exactly the same as aligning a receive antenna, except that the information regarding signal strength is referred to the transmitting site and acted upon there only.

Passive Repeater Orientation

Where passive repeaters are required, the process of getting the initial signal to the receiver may require some careful sighting, but once the signal is received, the process becomes one of sweeping the main lobe through its horizontal and vertical half-power points.

Antenna Reflector Orientation

The orientation of an antenna-reflector combination will require more care but can be accomplished in essentially the same manner as for the parabola. The movement of the main beam, however, is accomplished by the horizontal and vertical movement of the reflector. The proper illumination of the reflector is accomplished by movement of the vertically directed parabola.

It should be pointed out that most reflector-antenna combinations have rather strong side lobes, so care should be taken at all times to avoid leaving the antenna pattern on a side lobe.

Perhaps the best way to begin orientation of the combination is to be sure the parabola is properly illuminating the elevated reflector. This can be done reasonably well with the aid of a plumb line dropped from the center of the reflector to the center of the parabola. A spirit level can be used to determine roughly whether the parabola is pointing vertically.

The measurement technique used to determine the propagated signal strength is the same as that outlined previously. When the reflector has finally been positioned and oriented on the tower, it is best to rotate the exciting antenna in its mount while checking the received signal strength. Small amounts of rotation will cause large variations in received signal strength if the reflector is positioned on a side lobe. It should also be borne in mind that large degrees of rotation can be expected to result in cross polarization loss. In stubborn cases when multipath signals are also present, it may take an expert to tell the difference between the two. To prevent outages due to weather and adverse propagation conditions, however, the reflector should be positioned in the middle of its strong main lobe, and the antenna feed polarization should be oriented for maximum received signal.

Fixed Reflector Orientation

Most reflectors of the billboard type are quite difficult to locate accurately. The process is usually carried out on paper from an accurate knowledge of the location of the two terminals.

Since the adjustment of these devices is very limited, the pointing should be accomplished with great care; in most cases it is best to enlist the aid of a good surveyor.

When billboard-type reflectors are used, the path will usually result in line-of-sight transmission conditions for both legs. A transit can be set up at the site and the angles to each of the terminal locations very carefully measured. These angles can then be plotted for accurate location of the billboard reflector.

The reflector should be mounted in concrete to give it a firm foundation. If constructed in earth rather than rock, the foundations should be designed according to local building codes to prevent any movement of the reflecting surface during periods of freezing and thawing.

System Calculation and Proof of Path

System calculations that give proof of antenna alignment should be performed on each link of a microwave system. These calculations are usually simple enough to perform, consisting of simple addition and subtraction of gains and losses.

Measurements should be made carefully of the power output of the transmitter and the received signal level at the receiver. The transmitter output is commonly measured with a power meter designed for the proper level and frequency. Most of the meters used for this purpose are calibrated in dbm or watts, and the readings can be taken directly from the meter indication.

The receiver input power is usually measured by the substitution method, using the AGC voltage or the first limiter current as an indicator. A signal of known level is put into the receiver, and this level is increased or decreased until it agrees with the power received from the transmitter, as shown in Fig. 10-2. The generator power out, reduced by the loss in the attenuation, will give the level of the input power. A typical condition is as follows:

Gains		*Losses*	
Transmitter output power	+30 dbm	Free space	142
Transmitter antenna	38 db	Transmitter waveguide	1
Receiving antenna	38 db	Receiver waveguide	1
Receiver input power	−41 dbm	Miscellaneous waveguide	3
Total gain	147	Total loss	147

Transmitter output power is measured at the output before it goes to the antenna feed line. The antenna gains shown above are taken from Fig. 7-6 for a 6-foot antenna at 6 GHz. Receiver input is measured as indicated previously. Free space loss is taken from Fig. 9-5 for a 30-mile path. Transmitter and receiver waveguide loss are taken from Fig. 9-6 for the length of guide used. Miscellaneous losses are those resulting from waveguide flanges

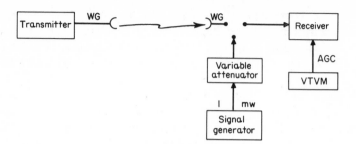

FIG. 10-2.   METHOD OF MEASURING RECEIVER INPUT POWER

and mismatches as well as minor variations in antenna gain; for most installations they will run about 3 db.

If the total gains and total losses do not match within ±3 db, the measurements should be repeated, and there may be cause to check the antenna orientation. Since propagation conditions are important to these measurements, they should be made when conditions are normal. If there is cause to suspect that conditions are not normal, the measurements should be repeated on another day.

Location of Obstructions

The main reason for calculating system losses and gains is to verify the path clearance. If an obstruction exists or if the path clearance brings about a strong reflection in one of the even numbered Fresnel zones, strong signal cancellation will result.

In most cases a path obstruction can be located by raising or lowering the antenna while measuring received power. Path test equipment is most convenient for this purpose because it is usually more portable and operates at higher frequencies.

Higher frequencies require a smaller antenna and result in a reduced spacing between the center line and the various Fresnel zones; to some extent this reduces the requirement for high towers. A permanent microwave system can be used, but the usual problems are feed-line flexibility, antenna size, and tower height.

Transmission measurements should be started with both antennas near the ground. They should be raised equally until free space conditions are reached. This elevation should be recorded and the antennas raised through the first Fresnel zone and into the sharp dip of the second as a check.

The free space elevation should be plotted on a path profile, and from this examination the offending obstruction may be obvious. In the event it is not easily determined, path measurements should be repeated with one antenna at the second zone level and the other started at the ground.

Index